The Mineral Kingdom

The Mineral Kingdom

by
Paul E. Desautels
Supervisor, Division of Mineralogy,
Smithsonian Institution

with photographs
by
Lee Boltin

A Ridge Press Book

Madison Square Press
Grosset
&
Dunlap
New York

Fred R. Sammis	Editorial Director
Doris Townsend	Editor
Evelyn Fiore	Associate Editor
John Sammis	Associate Editor
Harry Brocke	Art Director
Allan Mogel	Associate Art Director
Denis Adams	Assistant Art Director
Marilyn Weber	Production Manager

PRECEDING PAGES: *Copper dendrite from New South Wales, Australia.*
SUCCEEDING PAGES: *Adamite from Durango, Mexico.*

Contents

Introduction

This book is meant not as a highly methodical overview of all that is known of the mineral kingdom, but as an introduction to a very broad field of knowledge through a selected sampling of certain areas—a guided tour through some of its features, rather than a textbook lecture.

It is intended for the developing interests of the amateur: the museum buff hypnotized by the color and fire of a magnificent gem, the rockhound who spends his vacations exploring for specimens to add to his increasingly exciting collection, the student of technology, fascinated by the odd fact that in a computerized age some of the world's greatest riches are still being brought up from the earth's interior by half-naked men using hand- and foot-power, exactly as in the time of Solomon.

Fundamentally, it is written from the mineralogist's point of view, and, to the mineralogist, minerals are significant not merely because they produce a trayful of diamonds at Tiffany's or the silicon wafer that makes it possible to construct a radio inside a finger ring. The mineralogist sees the mineral kingdom as a changing, developing edifice based on solid substances. He is concerned with the geological processes that formed, and are still forming, these substances, and with the highly organized internal atomic structures that result in their being, by definition, crystals. Both geology and crystallography are extremely complex sciences, but some information about them has been outlined in this book (see Chapters 2 and 7) because it is important to anyone interested in learning more about this world of solid substances.

Most of the driving force for exploring and exploiting the mineral kingdom has come from the age-old demand for the raw materials of industry and the lure of exotic and valuable gemstones. Our technological civilization is totally dependent on mineral products wrested from nature. Gems, sought to satisfy the urge for owning objects both valuable and beautiful, are closely tied to man's cultural and political development. Oceans have been crossed and new territory conquered in their quest. Accordingly, both gemstones (see Chapter 3) and industrial minerals (see Chapter 8) have been given special attention.

Even aside from his need and desire for mineral materials, man's imagination has always been stimulated by the strange and wonderful things found among them. Some attract attention because of their great beauty. Others provoke curiosity through their strange appearance or behavior. A sampling of these striking and unusual minerals is given in Chapter 4, as well as, farther on, an introduction to classic items for collectors.

Naturally, no insight into the kingdom is complete without intimate glimpses of some of the places where noteworthy minerals have been found. The mining fields that are discussed in Chapter 5 differ in their histories and in the kinds of deposits they yield, and form a chain completely circling the globe the long way around from California to Australia.

Whatever man's contact with the mineral kingdom—for his science, his industry, or his cultural pursuits—the hope is that it will have been touched on in this book to a stimulating degree.

Paul E. Desautels

Myth, Fancy, and Fact

1

The fascinating facts about rocks and minerals are fair exchange for the ancient tales they replace

Four hundred years ago, in an age when murder by poison was a fine art, enemies of Benvenuto Cellini, the gifted Italian goldsmith, plotted to do away with him by mixing a powdered diamond with his food. Economy evidently was a factor, however, for at the last moment the assassins used a cheaper beryl instead—prompting Cellini later to record, triumphantly, that because diamond was not used "... the powder had no effect."

Cellini, who dealt constantly with precious stones, should have known that in fact the powdered diamond would have had no effect either, unless it had been served up in such quantity that he would have detected it as he chewed. But in the sixteenth century man's knowledge of the properties and characteristics of minerals was obviously uncertain.

Ancient man, of course, did know of the existence of the mineral kingdom. He started very early to accumulate information about it. He learned something about working metals and setting stones. But his knowledge was so thoroughly mixed with myth, superstition, and guesswork that even serious scholars of the more enlightened periods managed to hand down only a small body of reliable fact.

The most important early work on natural history was the thirty-seven volume *Historia Naturalis* written by Pliny the Elder (A.D. 23-79). In this, Pliny describes a long list of fabulous and mostly nonexistent stones, some of which were supposed to have originated in the stomachs of animals, as a result of the light of the moon, or by purge from the sea. Some of his stones were male, some female. Almost all possessed some sort of occult power. They kindled fires, quieted winds, increased intelligence, and in other ways influenced the unseen forces that were believed to surround man from birth to death.

Many real stones shared these mythical attributes. An amethyst pendant suspended on a dog-hair cord around the neck was supposed to be a guaranteed antidote for snakebite. Amethysts whose purple depths showed a pale, rosy glow enabled a drinker to ward off intoxication. Diamond was considered extremely powerful; while aware of its genuine attributes of hardness and fire resistance, Pliny—a man of his time—could also credit the notion that it protected the wearer against madness and violent fear. When a diamond was to be cleaved, gemworkers of Pliny's day first steeped it in goat's blood. This was supposed to make it fragile enough to split easily.

Among other inroads into genuine science, Pliny recognized several mineral species, including one he called "crystal," which is our quartz. With his contemporaries, he believed that this material occurred only in mountainous areas like the Alps, and was formed from moisture congealed by extreme cold. Pliny's mixture of verifiable fact enriched with unrecognized fantasy was typical of the "scientific" thinking of early periods.

The mineral kingdom abounds in curiosities that have caught man's attention from his first days on earth. One phenomenon that still excites superstitious speculation, and must have puzzled earlier men to the point of terror, is the meteorite. The ancient Jews held these mysterious objects in

PRECEDING PAGES: *A polished sample of jasper—fine-grained quartz—from Oregon resembles an unreal landscape. Varicolored iron and manganese impurities, trapped during formation, create the patterns.*

special reverence. They called them *Beth-el*—House of God—because they believed that the fallen fragments carried the blessings of God directly from heaven. These early Jews added other superstitions to mineral lore; among them was a story that one of King Solomon's rings was set with a stone of such peculiar power that he had only to gaze at it to know everything he needed to know at a given moment.

Magic rings were a fantasy common to many cultures. The Greek philosopher Appolonius of Tyna was reported to have possessed several, each set with a different metal or mineral. According to his contemporary, St. Justin Martyr, writing about A.D. 150, Appolonius could use his rings to calm the fury of the sea, hold back the winds of heaven, and tame wild animals instantly.

During the Middle Ages, the ancient superstitions formed a core around which many new ones collected. The toadstone, for example, was a widely accepted legend. It was supposed to be a stone endowed with medicinal powers, which could be extracted, by those who knew the proper rites, from the head of a toad. Both stone and

In his famous book De Re Metallica, *sixteenth-century scholar Georg Agricola included the earliest known illustration of ore prospecting by the use of divining rod—a process of which he disapproved.*

powers were completely apocryphal, of course, yet many respected writers of the period described how the toadstone worked to soothe toothaches, cure diseased kidneys, quiet stomach disorders, and burn the skin slightly if poison was nearby.

Even as late as the fourteenth century, Albertus Magnus, reflecting current ideas in his book *De Mineralibus et Rebus Metallicis*, felt it necessary to discuss whether or not stones had spirits. His conclusion was that they did not, but it ran counter to the general belief.

Magical stones, meanwhile, appeared and reappeared in contemporary folklore. At the beginning of the sixteenth century an Italian named Camillus Leonardus wrote a book about gems, in which he described an astonishing stone called an alectorius. This crystal-bright stone, about the size of a large bean, was allegedly carried in the body of a cock, and was mature and ready to be extracted when the cock refused to drink. Milo of Croton, a strong man of the sixth century, was supposed to have carried one constantly, and to have lost his strength only when he lost the stone.

The alectorius had numberless virtues. It banished thirst, made a wife more appealing to her

husband, and gave eloquence and persuasive power to its owner. It protected domestic peace and harmony, and attracted honor and victory. Clearly, it would have been a most desirable possession—had it existed.

Even during the Renaissance, that period of the highly touted "new learning," men like Paracelsus continued to expound a mixture of fact and fiction about the mineral kingdom. Paracelsus was a Swiss physician, alchemist, chemist, and lecturer, who introduced into Europe various new and effective mineral medicines—mercury, iron, and arsenic among them. However, he also believed in a metaphysical relationship between the mineral world and the planets and neighboring stars. According to these theories, the metals and minerals on earth had been thrown off by other planets, while the crystalline gem minerals, such as emerald and rock crystal, came to earth after having condensed on the nearer stars.

We still preserve traces of the old metaphysical notions that tie gems to the motions of the planets and stars, and suggest that they have control over human events. People still wear their birthstones, though not many moderns would admit that by so doing they are offering a hostage to fate. The Hope diamond, which now flashes gloriously in its display case in the Smithsonian Institution in Washington, was for years romanticized in the press as a jewel in whose wake misfortune trailed.

Yet despite the embroidery of fact with legend and folklore, the ancients managed to contribute much more than superstition to the development of mineralogy and metallurgy. Early experimentation produced a great deal of useful information. There is evidence that many early civilizations were familiar with the working of metal ores.

The shift of the center of civilization westward

FACING: *Crystal blades of blue kyanite from St. Gotthard, Switzerland, formed in a metamorphic environment.* ABOVE: *Botryoidal mimetite from a sedimentary environment in San Luis Potosí, Mexico.*

a

b

c

d

16

into Europe, some time before 1400 B.C., was most likely stimulated by the availability of iron ores and forests for the developing Iron Age. The Incas were working copper about 1000 B.C. King Solomon derived some of his glory from successful copper-mining operations carried on about 950 B.C. in what is now a desolate Israeli desert. Ancient China was certainly preparing metals for decorations and practical use at the same time as the Egyptians. The Greeks and Romans made wide use of copper and bronze for tools, coinage, weapons, and ornaments. In the new world, when the Muzo Indians of Colombia were conquered by Gonzalo Jiménez de Quesada in 1537, they offered him emeralds as a gift. These Indians, and their ancestors before them, had worked their emerald mines for so long that the history of the operation was lost in the mists of time. These isolated illustrations show that man began very early in his history to develop knowledge of the mineral kingdom, and to put it to practical use.

The long-accumulated, confused, and interwoven mass of fact and fantasy about minerals, gems, mining, and metals prevented the ancients from organizing any logical scheme of their nature. The facts, nevertheless, were there for later investigation when the political and cultural atmosphere was ready for development of scientific thought.

WHAT IS A MINERAL? A mineral is, first of all, something not belonging to the animal or vegetable kingdoms. Strictly speaking, this is a rather good definition, because it points out clearly that a mineral cannot owe its existence to living things. No definition of a mineral has yet been proposed that is all-inclusive and satisfying to everyone. With various slight modifications and elaborations, the traditional definition, appearing in most texts, states that a mineral is "a chemical element or compound occurring in nature as a result of inorganic processes." This is serviceable only if it is not interpreted narrowly. To gain a real understanding of it, the statement needs explanation and expansion.

The existence of chemical elements is one of the basic truths of all modern science. We know that the material universe is made up of a few more than a hundred fundamental elements. All the different kinds of things in all the kingdoms—animal, vegetable, mineral—are composed of these elements. They may be made of the pure element or of very complex combinations of elements. Some elements, such as gold, copper, iron, carbon, and oxygen, are well known. Others, such as lanthanum, xenon, and polonium, are primarily laboratory curiosities.

When these elements combine with each other, they are linked in small particles called atoms. An atom can be imagined as the smallest possible amount of the element that can exist. Atoms of each different element have a characteristic com-

FACING: *Medieval medicine from* Hortus Sanitatis *(1483)*—
(a) lapidary prepares stones; (b) toadstone is extracted and
(c) it draws out poison; (d) bloodstone cures nosebleed.
ABOVE: *Alchemist's triangle symbolized spirit, soul, body.*

bining ability; this controls the number of atoms that can enter into the combination.

For example, the element sulfur exists by itself in certain mineral deposits in the crust of the earth. It is a bright yellow, soft, resinous-looking substance that burns easily with a blue flame. However, sulfur can exist in combination with other elements, such as antimony. Usually three sulfur atoms unite with two antimony atoms. The chemist indicates this with the formula anti mony$_2$ sulfur$_3$ or, using his time-honored symbols, Sb_2S_3. The mineral name of this is stibnite; it is a bright, silvery, soft, metallic compound.

Sulfur may also combine with iron, thus form ing the mineral pyrite, FeS_2. If the same atoms are hooked together in a different arrangement

the mineral marcasite, also FeS_2, may be formed. Because they have the same composition although their atoms are joined in different ways, pyrite and marcasite are called polymorphs. There are other cases in which different element combina tions—for example, $CaCO_3$ (calcium carbonate, called calcite) and $MnCO_3$ (manganese carbonate, called rhodochrosite)—have their atoms joined in identical patterns. Such minerals are called iso morphs.

The first part of the traditional definition, then, speaks of elements and compounds, implying that the way the atoms combine to form different patterns is of primary importance. This idea is the basis of all really useful systems of grouping or classification of minerals. In all branches of science, attempts constantly are made to classify available facts. Unless they are related and compared with each other, however, such facts tend to remain isolated and sterile. Related to others, they lead to new ideas, new laws, and new understandings.

Attempts at trying to order and describe natural geological materials began early. About 300 B.C., Theophrastus, a Greek philosopher, wrote his book *On Stones*. Pliny's books, almost four hundred years later, included passages on gemstones, pigments, and important ores. In 1556 the famous *De Re Metallica* of Georg Agricola (the pen name of Georg Bauer), German scholar and mining authority, was published. His book brought up-to-date man's knowledge of mineralogy, mining, and the uses of metal ores.

The science of crystallography was given a bold start by Nicolaus Steno in 1669 with his astute observations on crystal measurement. By the middle of the eighteenth century, the allied sciences of mineralogy and chemistry were under

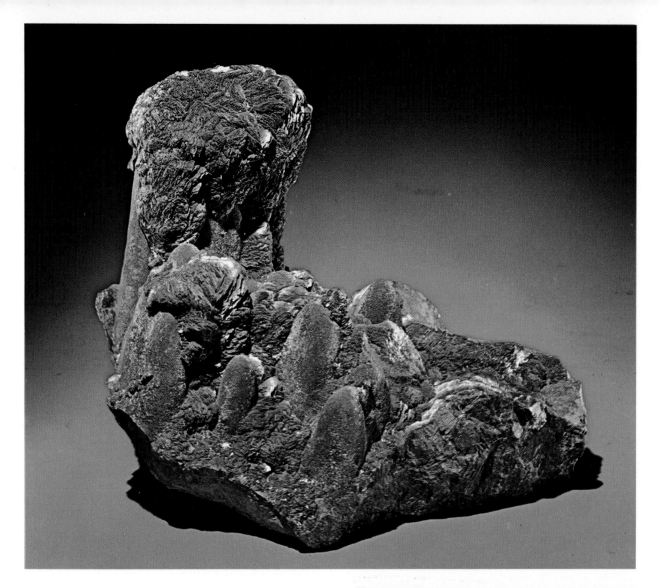

intensive investigation all over Europe. The transition was being made from superstition, myth, and conjecture about minerals. Increasingly, critical observation would now be applied to the mineral kingdom.

In 1774, the renowned Abraham Gottlob Werner, professor of mineralogy at Freiberg, Saxony, published his essay on the *External Characters of Minerals*. His ideas about the separation and grouping of known minerals by their external characteristics were spread rapidly by students, who came from all over Europe to study with him. The system of separating and arranging minerals according to their color, hardness, inflammability, and so on, seemed very logical. Relationships among the minerals were easier to see and new

FACING: *Ancient goldwork in a figurehead from a Viking ship*. THIS PAGE: *Stalactitic masses in widely differing forms—*TOP, *Marcasite crystals from Montreal, Wisconsin;* ABOVE, *Green malachite from the Congo.*

predictions about their chemical and physical behavior were easier to make.

In this same period, the French mineralogist René Just Haüy established an approach to the study of crystals that led directly to our modern understanding of them. His basic tenets are discussed in Chapter 2.

Finally, by the beginning of the nineteenth century, the Swedish chemist Berzelius had outlined a chemical classification of minerals. It was he who developed a theory of positive and negative kinds of atoms, which attract each other to form compounds. He showed that minerals are such compounds. Berzelius went on to publish a system of mineral arrangement based on many chemical analyses of minerals. In it, all the minerals of similar chemical composition, such as mercury sulfide (HgS) and lead sulfide (PbS), appeared as near neighbors.

It was not until 1854 that James Dwight Dana, professor of mineralogy at Yale, set the chemical classification of minerals on a firm footing. In 1837, Dana had published his first *System of Mineralogy*, using "a system of nomenclature constructed on the plan so advantageously pursued in Botany and Zoology." However, when the time came for the fourth edition of the monumental work in 1854, the author was forced to abandon this biological approach, which had been first established for botanical classification by Carolus Linnaeus of Sweden in the eighteenth century. More was known about the chemical nature of minerals; to show their relationships properly, Dana classified them in a purely chemical system. To this day, the primary classification system of the mineral species is based on their chemistry. From the 1854 edition of the *System* down through the current seventh edition, the increase in information about mineral structures obtained through use of X-rays has brought about the only major modification in Dana's system.

The discovery of X-rays in 1895 was to lead, in a few years, to development of the most powerful tool available for mineralogical studies. In 1912 Max von Laue, who had been a student of Wilhelm Konrad Röntgen, discoverer of X-rays, began experimenting with the application of X-rays to mineral crystals. He proved that X-rays were small enough to detect spaces between the atoms of which a crystal is made, and could be used to measure the arrangement of these atoms.

With the development of the science of X-ray crystallography, and the investigation of mineral crystal structures with X-ray gadgetry, it became obvious that chemical composition alone was not the answer to the nature of a mineral species. The arrangement of their atoms was revealed and recognized as being of extreme importance. Thus,

pyrite and marcasite, as before noted, are polymorphs—alike in chemical composition. But the different arrangement of their atoms results in their very different physical appearance and behavior.

Systems of mineralogy in wide use, prepared by prominent modern mineralogists, include those of Max Hey of England, Hugo Strunz of Germany, and Clifford Frondel of the United States. All of them take into account both the composition and atomic structure of mineral species. The systems are in many respects identical, differing only in incidentals.

In any classification system there is always a problem in applying names to the species. Minerals, unfortunately, have been overburdened with too many meaningless names accumulated through the centuries. For example, under the classification system devised by Sir John Hill in London in 1748, the mineral species pyrite was given several different names, based only on differences in shapes of the crystals—an effort at clarification that merely encouraged confusion.

The modern method of chemical-structural classification is far simpler and much more precise, although the names of many minerals in it are still scientifically meaningless. The naming of a new species has always been the privilege of the scientist first describing it. Consequently, species are named somewhat haphazardly for superficial appearance, noteworthy characteristics,

mode of occurrence, for people, places, and even political effect. Olivenite, for example, is named for its color, though a name based on its chemical-structural analysis would be far more significant. Reedmergnerite was named for two men, Reed and Mergner, of the United States Geological Survey. In recent years the species pravdaite, subsequently discredited, was named for the official Russian newspaper *Pravda*.

Nevertheless, to be given any name, and to be accepted as a distinct and separate species, a mineral must prove to be chemically or structurally different from any other known mineral. The distinguished mineralogists who make up the International Mineralogical Association have established a Mineral Names Commission, and set high standards for the scientific proof of a new species. In addition, research is carried on in many places to determine the status of those species that are in doubt. In older editions of Dana's *System of Mineralogy* more than three thousand mineral species are listed. The accepted number today is much nearer fifteen hundred. Several new species are discovered and approved each year, but at the same time several others are likely to be demoted to the status of mere varieties.

Sedimentation creates rich patterns. TOP: *Mud and limestone sediments form Italian marble slab.* ABOVE: *Sediments form flat marcasite concretion from Mazon Creek, Illinois—noted for fern fossils.*

MINERAL OCCURRENCE: As noted earlier, the commonly used definition for a mineral requires that it should occur in nature. This seems an obvious necessity until we remember that minerals are, after all, chemical elements and compounds. Many research scientists are engaged these days in preparing various kinds of chemical substances in the laboratory. Many of these substances are counterparts of some found in nature. It is common practice, in fact, for a mineralogist to prepare in a laboratory the species that he is studying in nature. This may be done to determine the natural temperature, pressure, or other conditions under which the mineral originally formed. It may even be necessary to manufacture a mineral because the natural supply is too scarce to provide enough specimens for a complete study. Prepared as a synthetic laboratory stand-in, the mineral can be studied by proxy.

Industry, of course, is always interested in the manufacture of synthetic minerals. Manufacture often creates a purer, more economical product than can be obtained by mining and processing the ores. Mineralogists have been devising techniques for producing synthetic minerals in the laboratory for more than two hundred years. These processes have been watched closely for possible use in making synthetic gemstones, since gems produce a high financial return for their weight and are difficult to find in nature.

Several problems arise if we hold strictly to the phrase "occurring in nature." The last mineral species listed in the second volume of Dana's *System of Mineralogy* is calclacite. This white, hairlike mineral was first found as a coating on limestone rocks and fossils stored in oak museum cases. Apparently, acetic acid derived from the oak wood of the cases, acting on these stored rocks

over a long period of time, had produced the new species. Although the process was natural enough, it would not have happened without the intervention of man, who accidentally brought together the raw materials. Perhaps the mineral species butlerite has more claim to natural origin but it too, and several others associated with it, are subject to question. Butlerite is a deep orange, glassy mineral occurring in small crystals. It is found at the United Verde copper mine at Jerome, Arizona. In this deposit it resulted from the gases formed during the burning of pyrite-bearing ore bodies. The process is a natural one, but it is likely that the underground fire would not have started had it not been for the activities of man.

When discussing the origin of solid parts of the earth's crust, the terms "rock" and "mineral" frequently become confused. For most purposes it is convenient to think of a rock as a solid made up entirely of a mixture of small bits of two or more different minerals. Sometimes a very large deposit of a single mineral species is accepted by the geologist as rock. In any case, these are solid substances that have occurred because the surface of the earth has been in a constant state of turmoil for untold centuries.

By human standards of time, of course, all the changes occur in very slow motion. Mountains have been thrust up, eroded away, cast into the sea. The process has repeated itself around the globe again and again and again. Parts of the crust have been repeatedly raised, lowered, buried, heated, cooled, flooded, ground up, compressed, carried here and there and never left in peace. As a result, it is a relatively rare thing to find a chunk of pure mineral that has not been intimately processed into some mixture of mineral grains which we call rock. Some of these natural processes, however, tend to isolate minerals and channel them into concentrated deposits. When this happens they can be mined, and become valuable to man.

WHERE MINERALS AND ROCKS FORM: Assuming that we ignore synthetic minerals and those of questionable origin, there remain perhaps eighteen hundred others that are found in nature. Geologists tend to group the environments in which minerals form as magmatic, sedimentary, and metamorphic. Meteorites have a nonearthly origin, and represent a special environment.

Minerals and rocks found in a *magmatic environment* are formed from melted, cooled material, and are called igneous rocks. Magma, the fiery liquid originating deep in the earth, now and then surges toward the surface. It almost seems that inconceivable internal pressures drive the molten liquid upward. Usually the magma stops short of the surface and cools, more or less slowly, leaving deposits that, because they formed within the earth, are called intrusive rocks. Sometimes the magma succeeds in reaching the surface and bursts forth into the air with a magnificent display of fireworks, devastating all about it with a roaring torrent of ash, fire, smoke, and molten material. This we call lava.

One fiery upsurge occurred on February 20, 1943, near Michoacan in West Central Mexico, where a farmer plowing his field was interrupted by a visit from the devil—or so he thought. From a fissure in the field smoke began to rise, and a roaring sound filled the countryside. The farmer

FACING: *Typical striations on jumble of pyrite cubes from Leadville, Colorado.* ABOVE: *Before James D. Dana's* System of Mineralogy *simplified classification, pyrite—like other minerals—had many names, confused identification.*

2*5*

was, in fact, witnessing the birth of Paricutin, a classic volcano. The volcano eventually spewed out enough ash and lava to devastate many square miles, destroy the local villages, and build a towering cone over one thousand feet tall.

Rocks that have formed on the earth's surface from cooling lava are called extrusive rocks. Lava thrown out by volcanoes cools so rapidly that separation of individual mineral grains has little time to occur. Lava rock, then, is not grainy but smooth-textured, sometimes even glassy. If glassy, it is called obsidian, and if dark in color but fine-grained, it is called basalt. One of the best examples of an occurrence of basalt is the Columbia Plateau in the northwestern United States. It was created by a long series of lava floods, which piled basalt layers more than five thousand feet thick over two hundred thousand square miles of Oregon, Washington, and Idaho.

Minerals and rocks found in a *sedimentary environment* are formed from those gravels, sands, and clays deposited—most frequently by water, but sometimes by wind or by glacial ice—in slowly building layers. Actually, the great bulk of rocks of the earth's crust is magmatic, formed from the cooling and solidification of molten material. This, however, is not obvious from a cursory examination of the rocks that show through the soil and plant covering that dusts the earth's surface. Almost all the rock formed from molten material is covered by a thin skim of sedimentary rock. This develops because surface rocks are constantly under the attack of weathering and erosion. Some products of this erosional attack—mud, sand, gravel—are carried off and deposited near and far after forceful separation from the mother rock. The rate of erosion is sufficient to lower the exposed solid parts of the earth one foot

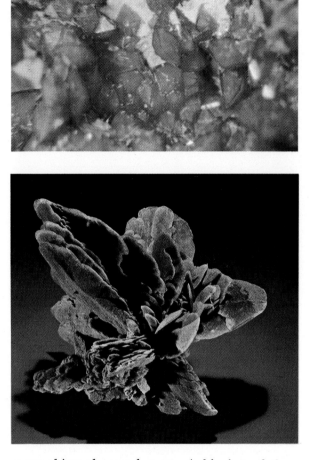

every thirty thousand years. A blanket of these ever-available sediments is always being deposited somewhere.

Ultimately the sediments are converted to rock by compression resulting from the weight of other sediments on top of the pile. This conversion, or lithification, can also be caused by cementing of the sediment particles. Cementing agents, usually quartz, limonite, or limestone, are carried in by water solution and deposited between the grains. Erosion may carry away some of its products in solution, and these solutions evaporate. Large deposits of limestone, gypsum, and other minerals trace their origin to such sedimentary processes.

Minerals and rocks found in a *metamorphic*

FACING: *Slow cooling of thick lava layer produced southern California's accidentally geometric basalt columns, which are not crystals.* THIS PAGE, TOP: *Microscopic butlerite crystals.* BELOW: *Gypsum from Chihuahua. Both are true crystals.*

27

environment have formed by changes in already existing rock. When any kind of rock is exposed to heat, pressure, liquids, and gases, it is changed—it becomes a metamorphic rock. Between the temperatures and pressures of an infernal molten environment and the watery grave of a sedimentary environment lies a great range of changing combinations of conditions. Changes in the existing rock to meet ever-changing environmental conditions create new kinds of metamorphic rocks and subsequent new minerals in the composition of these rocks.

The only solid-object samples we have that do not come from our planet are *meteorites*, which shoot into it from space. Meteorites are special kinds of rocks formed under special conditions. However, minerals of which they are made are the same kinds as those occurring on the earth. These fascinating objects can be conveniently divided into three groups: siderites (metallic), siderolites (stony and metallic), and aerolites (stony). By applying the same techniques used for the study of earthly rocks and minerals, the compositions of meteorites and the conditions under which they were formed can be determined. This information is valuable at a time when so much attention is being turned to space and planets. Diligent study may reveal geological processes which do, or do not, differ from our own; we may learn whether these processes occurred on larger planets or smaller, using raw materials similar to or different from ours.

HOW MINERALS AND ROCKS FORM: Whether the origin of rock be magmatic, sedimentary, or metamorphic, there are certain basic processes by which the rocks and the minerals that make them up are formed. The most important of these are: crystallization from molten material;

sublimation, or crystallization directly from a gas to a solid; formation from water solutions; metamorphism and metasomatism; weathering.

The kinds of minerals and rock mixtures that form depend in large part on the conditions under which they form. Because of this, there is an all-important law governing the entire event: At the time of its formation a mineral must be in equilibrium with its environment. This means that if pressures or other conditions change, even momentarily, then the kinds of minerals forming may also change. Even if the minerals have already formed before the change in growing conditions, they will still change in composition or structure. To exist in the end, the mineral must be perfectly adjusted to, or at least in satisfactory agreement with, its surroundings.

Crystallization from molten material: The kinds of materials formed from molten rock (or by any process for that matter) depend on the elements available. Surprisingly, of the approximately one hundred known elements, eight constitute 99 percent of the earth's rocks. Just two of these—silicon and oxygen—make up 74 percent, leaving only 25 percent for the other six—aluminum, sodium, calcium, iron, magnesium and potassium. This list easily accounts for our commonest commercial metals, aluminum and iron. Copper, zinc, gold, nickel, chromium and others are comparatively rare; in fact it is remarkable that nature has concentrated, in individual deposits, sufficient quantities of them to make it feasible for us to mine and use them.

As a magma cools and begins to form the solid crystals of minerals that make up igneous rocks, the liquid part remaining becomes richer and richer in less common elements and in water, carbon dioxide, other gases, and certain acids.

This residual hot liquid eventually cools and crystallizes in a unique manner. These last-formed minerals tend to be very coarse crystals, many of them of unusual size and composition. Such deposits are called pegmatites, and may range in size up to bodies that are thousands of feet long and hundreds of feet thick. Feldspar and mica are mined commercially from pegmatites, as are tourmaline, beryl, quartz, topaz, and other gem crystals. Pegmatites are also the source of many beautifully crystallized mineral specimens that become collectors' items. Over one hundred

FACING: *Specimen of obsidian—glassy volcanic rock—typical of those from Mexican occurrences.* ABOVE: *A nighttime eruption of Mexico's Paricutin. Volcanic bombs may contain rocks from great depths, providing valuable new study material.*

varieties of minerals have been found in pegmatites.

Sublimation: Some of the extremely hot gases in magma are released if they can find an avenue of escape to the surface through a gas vent, or fumarole. Some remain as gases and pass into the atmosphere. But frequently the contents of these gases, at the cool surface, pass directly from the very hot gas state to the solid state, without cooling through a liquid stage. This process is known as sublimation. Sulfur (S), fluorite (CaF_2), realgar (AsS), halite (NaCl), hematite (Fe_2O_3) and others have been found formed directly from hot gases by sublimation. Commercial ores are seldom deposited this way, but sublimed sulfur and halite have been mined.

Formation from water solutions: Minerals that form from water solutions are known as evaporites. In every case evaporite deposits occur when mineral-bearing water evaporates. In arid and semi-arid regions, lakes, or large bodies of water left by drainage into a basin, are very temporary. They evaporate and leave behind a mineral crust. Water accumulates again with the rains, and the annually repeated process gradually builds up thick deposits of evaporite.

The great Atacama Desert of Chile is an extremely arid area, six hundred miles long, on the border of northern Chile and Peru. In this desert, one thirty-second of an inch of rain for the year is considered above average. In some places it never rains. Here there are very rich deposits of soluble copper minerals and also very large beds of soluble nitrates. At one time this area was the world's major source of nitrates for fertilizer and for the manufacture of explosives.

With normal rainfall, such deposits would long since have been dissolved and run off into the Pacific Ocean. As a matter of fact, the peculiar evaporation process by which they are thought to form could not operate. In arid regions like the Atacama Desert, underground waters carrying dissolved minerals seep slowly upward toward the surface and quickly evaporate, leaving the minerals deposited on the surface. Constant upward seepage and continual rapid evaporation gradually build the surface deposit, and no rain washes it away.

Underground water, with its dissolved mineral burden, can also migrate into underground caves or other openings. As the liquids drip into these cavities the changes in temperature and pressure cause the water to evaporate or its contents to change by giving off gases. The resulting deposits form stalactites, stalagmites, pillars, and other subterranean sculptures.

Metamorphism and metasomatism: According to the previously stated law, a mineral must be in equilibrium with its environment. When nature, in its laboratory, changes some rocks into others, it operates in one of two ways: new materials are added to the original rocks, or the original materials merely are rearranged. Metamorphism occurs in both ways.

Geologists differentiate between contact metamorphism and regional metamorphism. The first occurs when the earth strains and shifts, and new intrusions of magma force up into already stable country rock. Heat, pressure, and the dissolving action of actual contact with magma cause the surrounding rock to change. Also, hot liquids and gases emanate from the magma and penetrate the surrounding rock. This causes additional changes, which are more extreme near the magma and taper off with distance from it. Metamorphism caused by penetration of these hot liquids and gases is given the special name of metasomatism.

a

b

e

d

g

Each of the three geologic environments in which rocks form produces many different kinds of rocks. Shown here, from a metamorphic environment, are: (a) marble and gneiss from Moravia; (b) schist, granulite, meta-diorite

from Egypt and Moravia; (c) brecciated marble and limestone from Italy and Spain; (d) brecciated marble and limestone from Italy, Sicily. From a magmatic environment: (e) porphyry and granite from Italy, Egypt, Rumania. From a sedimentary environment: (f) limestone from Sicily and Austria; conglomerate from Italy; (g) limestone from Spain, Sicily, Italy, Bohemia.

31

Regional metamorphism describes itself. It is caused by large-scale changes in the earth's crust, and may extend over thousands of square miles. The buckling and thrusting of the crust that resulted in the dramatic birth of the Appalachian Mountains millions of years ago shortened the distance between what are now Baltimore and Pittsburgh by perhaps two hundred fifty miles. The forces necessary to move such vast tonnages of rock and thrust them thousands of feet into the air are incomprehensible. Yet this occurs again and again. Little wonder that the rocks in such regions are stressed beyond endurance, and change themselves to meet the demands made upon them.

Dynamic motion of the earth's crust is not a requirement for regional metamorphism. The slow, undramatic, but continuous building of layers of sediment, century after century, can have the same effect. Water pressure five miles under the sea is about twelve thousand pounds per square inch. Imagine the pressure under five miles of rock sediment, which is three times as dense. These rocks will alter to suit the new environment.

Weathering: There is a tendency to accept the notion that rainwater "just wears away the rock." By itself, water works very slowly in its attack on rock—unless, of course, it rushes past carrying sand grains and gravels that grind and scratch as they tumble along. The devastating effect of rain as a weathering agent is due to the dissolved gases—oxygen and carbon dioxide—which it carries along from its falling passage through the atmosphere. These dissolved gases turn rain into a very weak acid which, over a period of time, chemically attacks the various minerals, converting them to new chemical substances which in turn attack their neighbors. Thus the original integrity of the rock, ore, or mineral is destroyed.

TOP: *In Bryce Canyon, Utah, sculptured appearance of eroded remnants was produced by uneven weathering.* ABOVE: *Agate rim, amethyst crystals in geode from Rio Grande do Sul, Brazil.*

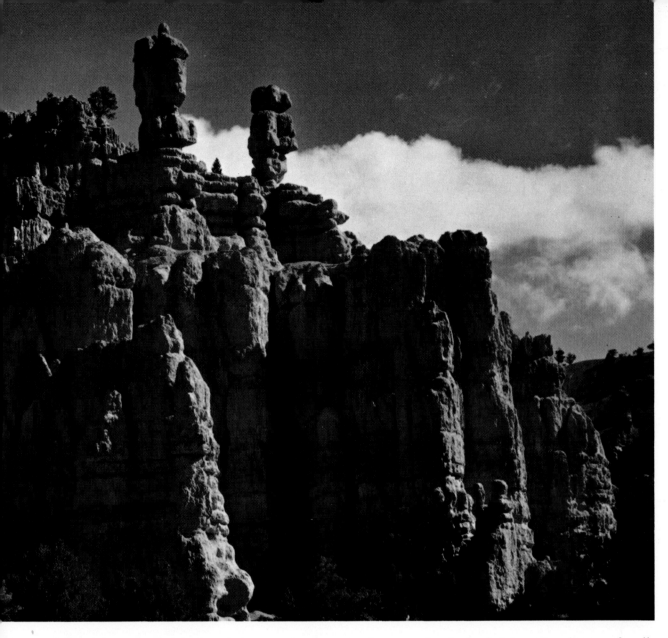

The rich copper deposits of Arizona became commercially valuable only because of centuries of downward chemical leaching, or dissolving, of low-grade copper minerals. These were gradually redeposited in more concentrated form deep in the deposit. Later, as erosion progressed, the deep, enriched ores were exposed for exploitation of the scarce and valuable metal.

All of the geological processes and environments mentioned are related to each other in unbridled complexity. Feldspar is one of the most abundant minerals formed from magma. When it is exposed and weathered it is readily converted into clay. Deposits of sedimentary clays, when they are deeply buried by other layers of sediments, react to the great increase of pressure and temperature by changing to metamorphic muscovite and garnet. Then they are stable in their new environment until erosion starts the chain again.

It is obvious now that expansion of the definition "occurring in nature" as a result of "inorganic process" is a science in itself again.

The mineral kingdom is extensive, varied and still largely unknown. Science is exploring it actively, industry is exploiting it eagerly—but the chances are that nature, which is constantly busy changing and renewing it, will always be one step ahead in this chain of events.

Flowers of the Kingdom

2

*Outwardly, a crystal may be
dazzling or dull, but its precise
internal order is always beautiful*

For the physicist the words "crystal" and "solid" carry the same meaning, because all solids have the internal organization of atoms comprising crystal structures. Since all minerals are solids and all solids are crystals, then all minerals are, obviously, crystals. The study of crystals therefore is essential to an understanding of all the inhabitants of the mineral kingdom.

The term "flowers of the kingdom" was first used by the renowned crystallographer Abbé René Just Haüy of France. He was referring to externally well-formed natural crystals of minerals, those remarkable objects that often seem as brilliant and sparkling as the gemstones that may be cut from them. It is not unusual for natural crystals to be so geometric in appearance that they seem to have been cut by some master craftsman for use as models in a study of solid geometry. The formation of crystals is an expression of natural laws, and outward evidence of marvelous atomic activity that has created their intricate structures.

The word crystal is derived from the Greek word *krystallos*, which in turn comes from *kryos*, meaning icy cold. The Greeks believed that crystals of quartz resulted from ice having frozen so hard it would never thaw out. Although the name was first used only for quartz, it came through the centuries to include all crystals and even some kinds of manufactured glass. This glass, used for goblets and other tableware, looks like quartz, but it is not crystal at all. A crystal is a solid, geometric object which has, under suitable growth conditions, an external form composed of a number of related, flat faces. Its form is the outside expression or evidence of a very highly organized internal arrangement of atoms in tiny units stacked together. All true crystal is made this way.

All so-called crystal, then, is not crystal. The word has a very precise meaning, which is universally understood in the various sciences. Why is it incorrect to call cut-glass tableware crystal? It certainly seems to be solid, and it has an appearance similar to that of some natural crystals. It might actually be truly crystalline if it were a solid substance. But, strange as it seems, glass is a liquid.

The physicist recognizes three forms in which the materials of the universe can exist: solids, liquids, and gases. The major differences in the three states are due to the differences in energy of their atoms. Gas atoms are the most energetic, active, and widely spaced, and have little control over their mutual destinies. Liquid atoms, on the other hand, try to group themselves but, being still too energetic, slip past each other. The atoms are spaced somewhat apart, and lack overall organization among themselves. Solid atoms have comparatively little energy; they are closely spaced, and therefore they force each other into organized patterns.

Glass is a liquid, then, which becomes glass when the atoms in the liquid are suddenly reduced to the energy level of a solid before they have a chance to get organized. Glass atoms become locked in a chaotic mass. In time they may organize themselves and become true crystal solids.

PRECEDING PAGES: *Crystal models, used in the study of natural crystals, are cut from many materials. These models are of the high-quality glass popularly, but incorrectly, called "crystal."*

TOP: *Pyrite cubes—an intergrown mass
from Ambeseguas, Spain.* ABOVE: *Parallel
growth in amazonite crystals, a feldspar
variety, from Pike's Peak, Colorado.*

37

But this happens far too slowly to be noticeable.

The real beginning of the science of crystallography came in the sixteenth century with the publications of the mathematician, Johannes Kepler. He wrote dissertations on the subject of geometrical solids, and derived mathematically a series of solid forms identical with those found among minerals. In 1611 he published a paper that explained the uniformly hexagonal shape of snow crystals as an orderly arrangement of smaller units composing the crystals. About the same time, Athanasius Kircher advanced the proposition that there was some kind of internal force in crystals causing them to develop outward along certain fixed directions.

In 1669 Nicolaus Steno established the first law of the science of crystallography. This fundamental law—The Constancy of Interfacial Angles—seemed simple, but was actually a very profound observation. It stated that for any crystals of a given mineral, the angles measured between the same sets of crystal faces were always exactly the same. Any crystal of quartz, for instance, no matter how lopsidedly grown or malformed or large or small, when measured with a simple instrument called a goniometer—*gonio* meaning angle and *meter* meaning measure—could be proved to have universally identical sets of angles. Steno's work was based on an accumulation of rather crude measurements on quartz crystals. But by 1783 Romé de Lisle, a French crystallographer, had measured an enormous number of crystals with some accuracy and substantiated Steno's law.

The science of crystallography received its final push up to modern times from the Abbé Haüy during this same period. Haüy, honorary canon of the Cathedral of Notre Dame, was a professor at the Museum of Natural History in Paris. In his *Traité de Minéralogie* he was the first to develop the important fundamental notion that every crystal is built up by an orderly stacking of tiny sub-units, and that the final shape of the crystal depends both on the shape of these small units and the way they are packed together.

Startling scientific discoveries are rarely made by accident. They are made rather by men who are mentally prepared to observe and interpret anything they experience. However, legend has it that Haüy, while examining a collection at the home of a friend, dropped a specimen of calcite. Gathering together the ruins, Haüy noticed that the broken pieces were all quite similar and resembled other calcite crystals he had seen. With an exclamation of *"Tout est trouvé!"* — (All is discovered!)—he returned to his laboratory and systematically demolished all the different shapes of calcite crystals he could find in a successful effort to prove his point.

No matter what the shape of the parent crystal, the broken-down pieces all had faces at the same angles, each one being a rhombohedron—a parallelepiped whose bases are all parallelograms. Haüy found that he could continue cleaving each of these pieces until it was too small to handle, with the same results. He reasoned that eventually there would be a limit to the size of the pieces that would break out in this regular shape, and concluded that every calcite crystal is made of thousands of very tiny rhombohedrons.

Not stopping there, Abbé Haüy boldly explained the fact that all calcite crystals are not the same shape on the outside. He did this by assuming that at the surface of the crystal the units could be progressively staggered to form a developing series of steps in the direction of the crystal faces. How, then, could the faces be so smooth if they were composed of steps? Since the units were very small the eye could not distinguish the steps. As a matter of fact, later X-ray work showed the units to be about one hundred millionth of an inch long; the unaided human eye can normally distinguish only objects about one million times larger.

Out of this theory, Haüy next developed a system of axes, which can be used to measure a crystal face by the way each face cuts each axis used for describing each particular crystal. He developed this system into the Law of Simple Rational Intercepts, which has been known ever since as Haüy's Law.

In 1850, Monsieur Bravais, a mathematician, showed the possible patterns that could be made from a series of points arranged symmetrically in space. These fourteen possible groupings, known as the Bravais lattices, are still essential for understanding modern X-ray crystallography.

In 1912 Max von Laue used X-rays to study crystals, and was able to confirm that everything Haüy had proposed was essentially true. Crystals are actually made up of very tiny units in an orderly arrangement. The units are much smaller than Haüy ever dreamed, but they follow his ideas closely and make his law valid. The arrangements closely parallel the Bravais lattices. Later work by the father-and-son team of English physicists, W. H. Bragg and W. L. Bragg, refined von Laue's work; they showed that these crystal lattices existed and were caused by precise, orderly placement of the atoms of a crystal.

Mineral elements are not uniformly distributed throughout the crust of the earth but have been concentrated by various geological processes in particular places. These concentrations or deposits constitute the natural resources of mineral materials, which we exploit for science and industry. It is in these concentrations that a sufficient number of atoms of elements accumulate to form crystals. The crystal-growing process begins and the atoms go through a series of energy and position changes that will ultimately produce the solid. Let us see what these processes are.

Much of the activity, physical and chemical, that we observe on the earth requires a loss of energy. An automobile runs by using up or "losing" energy stored in its gas tank. A windup alarm clock runs and rings by using up the energy stored in its wound springs. In the same way, a crystal can form by the accumulation of atoms

FACING: *Abbé René Just Haüy was the first mineralogist to suggest that crystals had orderly internal structure.*
ABOVE: *Early goniometers*—LEFT, *contact type, 1780;* RIGHT, *reflecting type, 1809—gave fairly precise crystal measurements.*

only if the atoms lose some of their energy. Melts, solutions, and gases are the source of all the very active atoms that make up crystals. Atoms found in hot, melted materials as gases or in solutions are extremely active, moving about at tremendous velocities. They are packed with energy, which exhibits itself as rapid motion. The atoms that are locked up in solids are not available unless the solids can be melted, dissolved, or vaporized, or unless energy can in some way be added to the atoms to turn them loose.

Crystals are formed when cooling gas or vapor atoms slow down, get closer together, grasp each other with strongly attractive forces, and become locked in a regimented order. Every snowfall illustrates this beautifully. When the air, heavy with water vapor, cools sufficiently, atomic groups composing the water vapor slow down and finally lock each other into the beautiful hexagonal patterns of snow crystals. Sometimes the shift from vapor to crystal occurs as a two-step event. First the atoms slow down, so that the vapor becomes a liquid. Then the atoms continue to decrease their activity until they actually grasp each other tightly in a solid embrace. The process of losing energy and organizing a solid structure is the same for atoms in melts and solutions.

Atoms in solution, like those in gases, can be formed into crystals by cooling the solution to remove energy. Crystals can also start to form when some of the water, or other solvent, is removed by evaporation. The atoms of water in a water solution of salt, for example, have an average energy of motion. However, a few of them are more energetic than the average. Now and then some of the overenergetic ones move so rapidly that they escape the solution and

move into the surrounding air, taking along their extra supply of energy. This leaves the entire solution a little poorer in energy than it was. The smaller, less energetic amount of water still left in the solution interferes less with the process of forming salt crystals. The atoms composing the salt move closer together and formation of solid salt crystals begins.

The earth is constantly surrounded by an envelope of gases and is constantly evaporating water from its surface. The earth is also constantly forming new solutions by movement of water on and in its crust, and is periodically forcing molten rock toward the surface. Thus there is always a ready supply of vapors, solutions, and melts for the continuous formation of new crystals.

Because it is possible to reproduce some of nature's conditions in the laboratory, a number of rather ingenious methods have been invented

Quartz, one of the commonest minerals, occurs in many varieties. Here, two specimens from Mexico. FACING: *Sculpture-like agate from Chihuahua.* ABOVE: *Amethyst from Vera Cruz.*

for growing synthetic crystals. The only differences seem to be that nature uses less pure materials, operates on a vastly larger scale, and has unlimited amounts of time.

In the laboratory, good crystals are usually grown from melts or solutions. One of the basic techniques used is the flame-fusion process invented by a French chemist, Auguste Victor Louis Verneuil. He developed an ingenious chalumeau—an upside-down blowpipe—which was immediately successful in making remarkably good ruby. Today, rubies cut from this material are very superior in color, clarity, and size to almost all natural rubies. Chemically and structurally—even under X-ray examination—these gems are identical with their natural counterparts.

Other crystal-manufacturing methods use solutions of the substances to be formed. Many minerals do not dissolve well in water. To overcome this difficulty, other dissolving agents or fluxes are used at high temperatures, as in the technique developed by the Bell Telephone Laboratories for growing synthetic ruby. A platinum container about ten inches high and six inches in diameter is filled with a flux of eleven pounds of lead oxide (PbO) and fourteen ounces of boron oxide (B_2O_3). To this is added the material for making the ruby itself: twenty-six ounces of aluminum oxide (Al_2O_3) and just a trace of chromium oxide (Cr_2O_3) to give a red color. The container and its charge are then heated in an electric furnace to 2400 degrees Fahrenheit, so that the chromium oxide and aluminum oxide dissolve in the now liquid flux. During six hours of heating at this temperature the contents are stirred continuously by rotating the pot first one way and then the other. After six hours, the temperature is slowly and evenly dropped about 170 degrees Fahrenheit per day for several days. As the temperature drops just below 2260 degrees Fahrenheit, ruby crystals begin to form. When cooling is finished and the whole mass has become solid, with the new ruby crystals mixed in it, the flux is dissolved by soaking in nitric acid, which has no effect on the ruby crystals.

Another useful technique for growing crystals from a high-temperature melt was originated in 1918, but was not developed and used until 1926. Lately it has been used to grow silicon and germanium single crystals for use in transistors. For this purpose, the container is made of temperature-resistant platinum or some other metal, such as iridium or rhodium. It is heated and loaded with the powdered material from which the crystal is made. A small crystal of the metal to be crystallized, perhaps germanium, is suspended

over the now melted germanium on the end of a rapidly rotating shaft. It is then lowered carefully and allowed, while still rotating, to touch the surface of the liquid germanium. Still rotating, the original germanium sample is raised very slowly, revealing a new growth upon the seed crystal, a growth that increases in dimension as the shaft rises. It looks almost as if a cylindrical crystal of the metal is being pulled up out of the liquid. Such "pulled" single crystals can be grown to remarkable lengths. Using this method, Dr. Kurt Nassau of Bell Telephone Laboratories grew a crystal of scheelite ($CaWO_4$) that eventually reached a length of eighteen inches.

Usable crystals can be grown also from water solution in the laboratory. Usually very high temperatures and pressures are needed to get the various substances into solution. Large quantities of valuable quartz crystals are grown this way for use in the electronics industry. Because water and heat are essential to the process, it is called a hydrothermal method—*hydro* meaning water and *thermal* meaning heat. Equivalent natural quartz of the type that is laboratory-grown is so rare and so expensive that it is economically sounder to manufacture it. Pressures up to fifty thousand pounds per square inch are used at temperatures of as much as 1300 degrees Fahrenheit, and substances are present to help the quartz go into solution.

Under these extreme conditions the autoclaves or "bombs" containing the solution must be extremely strong. They must have leakproof and blowout-proof closure devices and must be silver- or platinum-lined to prevent contamination of the solution by chemical attack on the lining by the mineralizer. Usually about six inches in diameter and twelve feet long, industrial bombs

FACING: *Snow crystals—a reproduction from the rare* Les Pierres Précieuses *by J. P. Rambosson (1870).* ABOVE: *A high tridymite structure model representing tridymite that has crystallized at a temperature higher than normal.*

a small cluster of atoms will come together and make a starting unit or seed. Sometimes only a few seeds form, and the resulting crystals are large and externally well formed, with distinct crystal faces. If many seeds suddenly form, the result will be an interlocking mass of small crystals showing no particular external characteristics. Such a mass is considered crystalline, but not a crystal.

As the atoms of a crystal begin to cluster, they are forced into positions related to each other in a highly organized manner. The positions taken depend mostly upon two things—the size of the atoms and the amount of attraction they have for each other. The atoms build themselves up into three-dimensional networks of repeating patterns, some of which are quite simple and others very complex. These are called the space lattices and, as Bravais had predicted, there are only fourteen different lattices possible. All others are merely variations of the fourteen arrangements.

A close look at the space lattice of any crystal shows that it consists of a unit arrangement of atoms that is repeated many times through space to make up the total lattice. This tiny, three-dimensional unit is called a unit cell. It is the shape and symmetry of this unit cell, repeated again and again, that ultimately determines the shape and symmetry of the final crystal. Sometimes the actual shape of the unit cell appears as the outside shape of the crystal. At other times the external faces do not seem related to the shape of the unit cell. Actually, they are always precisely related to it. A crystal face is nothing more than a flat surface made of tremendous numbers of atoms all arranged in the same plane. Since each plane of atoms is a potential crystal face,

have four-inch-thick walls that are made of cold-rolled steel.

The bomb is loaded with water, mineralizer, and a quantity of small pieces of pure natural quartz in the bottom. At the upper part of the bomb are hung the seed crystals of quartz cut in the form of flat plates. The bomb is sealed and heated electrically to crystallization temperature. The pressure automatically rises tremendously because of the heat-expanded contents. After about twenty days the cycle ends; all the small pieces of natural quartz from the bottom have been dissolved in the water solution and redeposited on the surface of the seed crystals to make fat new crystals of quartz.

If man or nature has provided the proper conditions and sufficient material to make a crystal,

Examples of well-crystallized minerals. above: *Exceptional orthorhombic crystal of sulfur from Agrigento, Sicily.* facing, top: *Iron-stained hexagonal calcite, Cumberland, England.* right: *Cockscomb colony of small orthorhombic marcasite crystals, Picher, Oklahoma.*

several different combinations of faces are possible for the crystal. It may not end up, therefore, being exactly the same shape as the unit cell, but may exhibit faces represented by any prominent plane of atoms in its space lattice.

Today's mineralogist studies space lattices and unit cells by using modern X-ray techniques. X-ray studies tell us a great deal about the possible arrangement of the space lattice in a crystal. However, they do not make absolutely certain the choice among the few possible lattices for a given crystal. Other evidence is needed. The study of crystal morphology is a highly developed science, which explores the external shapes of crystals and the relationships that exist among those shapes.

When a crystal has a *plane of symmetry* it means that an imaginary plane passed through it will divide it into two halves that are exact mirror images of each other. To discover an *axis of symmetry*, a crystal is rotated or spun on an imaginary axis passed through it. If, during a complete turn on this axis, the crystal assumes at least one position that makes it look identical with the way it started out, then an axis of symmetry is present. This kind of crystal symmetry can occur two, three, four, or six times for one turn on the axis, depending on the species of the crystal. A crystal is symmetrical about its theoretical center—or has a *center of symmetry*—if any line drawn through this center point always intersects the opposite faces of the crystal at identical distances from the center point.

The detailed measurement of thousands of crystals with improved instruments has resulted in the determination of just which planes, axes, and centers exist together, in combination, in natural and synthetic crystals. All crystals can be conveniently and logically grouped or classified into only thirty-two different kinds of symmetry, or crystal classes. For the sake of further convenience and logic, these thirty-two classes are grouped into six crystal systems, all classes in a given system having some important symmetry in common.

The systems are: isometric, tetragonal, orthorhombic, monoclinic, triclinic, and hexagonal. Each system is recognizable by a set of unique symmetry axes assigned to it and by means of which its symmetry family can be easily described. On page 47, block models of typical crystals in each of these six systems are pictured, with diagrams describing their axes.

A set of identical faces on a crystal is called a form. Everyone recognizes the cube, a form belonging to the isometric system. It consists of a set of six faces, each one pierced at right angles by a crystal axis and each one exactly like the others. Another form in the isometric system is the octahedron. This form consists of eight faces, each an identical equilateral triangle. The faces are positioned so that the octahedron looks like a double-ended square pyramid.

Fighting the multitude during the rush hour in the New York subways or boarding a Japanese train with the help of an official "pusher" can give some insight into the problems an atom has in occupying its place within a crystal lattice. When the rush starts and the seats begin to fill, some of the seats and some of the standing spaces are improperly used: two people are crowded in where only one fits, or perhaps someone is occupying a space and a half. The result is a dislocation of proper packing.

Since the growing of a typical crystal requires the proper placement of about sixteen trillion

(a) Isometric System
Axes equal length
All angles 90°

(b) Tetragonal System
Horizontal axes equal length
All angles 90°

(c) Orthorhombic System
Axes different lengths
All angles 90°

(d) Monoclinic System
Axes different lengths
Angle larger than 90°

(e) Triclinic System
Axes different lengths
No angles 90°

(f) Hexagonal System
Horizontal axes equal length
Legs 60° apart

Crystal-forming atoms organize in one of the six crystal systems shown, with characteristic symmetry axes. Typical minerals in each crystal system are: (a) pyrite, fluorite; (b) zircon, rutile; (c) barite, sulfur; (d) sphene, gypsum; (e) axinite, rhodonite; (f) quartz, calcite.

atoms an hour, the number of defects in the packing tends to be phenomenal. But even more phenomenal is the number of atoms that do manage to get into the right places. A normal accumulation of defects resulting from the organization of a crystal is only about one-hundredth of one percent—far better than the subways manage.

One way to reduce defects in man-made crystals is to slow down drastically the rate of packing. But even if the rate is slowed to one-tenth of normal, more than one and a half trillion atoms must still be packed in the crystal in an hour. A better solution is to slow down the packing rate, or crystal growth, just enough to see what causes the defects in placement, thereby learning to change the conditions so as to avoid creating these defects. This is one method currently in use for studies of crystal growth. This slowdown can be accomplished by using solutions with less material in them or by controlling the rate of temperature reduction. But whatever the rate of growth, crystals are always subject to problems that cause structural disorder.

One convenient way to look at the various disorders in crystals is to arrange them by point disorders, line disorders, plane disorders, and solid or three-dimensional disorders.

By *point disorders* we mean that certain points in the space lattice are not properly occupied. Quite often, the liquids or gases from which crystals come are impure, and the atoms of the impurity happen to be about the same size as the atoms that will form the crystal, thereby being able to occupy positions in the lattice normally used by the proper atoms. The structure thus develops normally, but the final crystal is of mixed composition. The mineralogist refers to this as a mixed crystal, or a solid solution. Mixing can

proceed to a remarkable extent if the sizes of the atoms do not differ more than 15 percent.

One of the best examples of mixing occurs in the mineral species fayalite and forsterite. Fayalite is an iron silicate and forsterite a magnesium silicate. They have closely related structures. In nature, a complete series of their combined crystals can be found with almost any proportions of iron and magnesium. Of course, this mixing causes changes in characteristics, and in the case of the fayalite-forsterite series a crude separation can be made just on the basis of color. Crystals of compositions toward the forsterite or magnesium end of the series are light-colored greenish-brown, green, or even white. Toward the fayalite or iron end of the series the crystals are dark greenish-brown, brown, or black.

Point disorder can be of another type. Crystals, unlike living objects, do all their growing by adding new material in layers of atoms on the outside of the crystal. This is called growth by accretion. In the hustle and bustle of trying to get hundreds of layers of trillions of atoms quickly and accurately set in place, it is very easy for some new layers to be deposited before all the lattice positions underneath are fully occupied. This means that many atom positions in a crystal are really occupied by a ball of nothing. These empty spots are called voids. An excellent example of this is the mineral pyrrhotite, a combination of iron and sulfur. When analyzed chemically, this mineral was described as solid solution or mixed crystal, with an excess of sulfur in the normal iron sulfide. It turned out, however, that there was not too much sulfur but too little iron. Many of the positions in the lattice that should be occupied by iron atoms were vacant. The realization that many such minerals have voids in their structures

FACING: *Pyrolusite, a black manganese oxide, sometimes grows as branching crystal dendrites embedded in sedimentary rocks. This remarkably fernlike sample is in shale from Solenhofen, Germany.*

49

has helped to explain a number of puzzling chemical compositions.

There is still another kind of point disorder which is related to that found in mixed crystals. Sometimes the impurity atoms may be very much smaller than those in the lattice. If so, they can easily slip into spaces among the atoms of the lattice, which is such an open network that there is plenty of room between occupied spaces. Metal crystals very often take up atoms of hydrogen, carbon, boron, and nitrogen—all small atoms—in these spaces. In structures of the amphibole family of minerals there are holes in the network that are large enough to take in sodium atoms.

Plane disorders are another common occurrence. Mention has already been made of crystalline masses, made up of groups of crystals that form together as touching grains rather than as freestanding individuals. There is often disorder in the planes of atoms that are located at the boundaries where the grains touch.

A grain boundary appears to be a no man's land between two crystal grains. The problem is that atomic planes do exist at the boundary, but the atoms in these planes have a difficult time deciding which crystal's structure they should be lined up with. The obvious solution prevails: some of the atoms align themselves with one crystal and some with the other, so that for several layers there is disorder.

Even with a freestanding, well-developed single crystal, there is often the same sort of disorder on the outside layers. Atoms in these layers are in a different situation from that of their colleagues at the interior of the crystal. In the interior all the atoms are totally surrounded by others. On the surface the atoms have no layers over them and are, therefore, relatively more free. Since much of the influence of nearby atoms is missing, these surface atoms are slightly more active and will be forced into somewhat different positions. They are also more susceptible to chemical activity and to removal from the surface of the crystal. Every time a crystal breaks, in fact, some of its interior layers are exposed. The atoms in these newly exposed layers must now shift positions and make other adjustments to fill a role somewhat disordered from the pattern of the rest of the structure.

Line disorders caused by improper placement of lines of atoms, rather than points or planes, have great effect on the growth of crystals. When extra lines of atoms are trapped in a structure in its pell-mell building rush, they obviously must force it out of alignment. It may be many atom layers later before the structure is able to compensate to straighten out the ripples. Since there are so many of these dislocations, some manage to cancel each other out, while others tend to add their effects and make the situation worse. An accumulation of dislocations can stress and weaken severely the structure of a crystal.

Strangely enough, surface dislocations on a crystal can encourage it to grow more easily and more rapidly. This is because an atom, when it prepares to become part of a crystal structure, may attempt to attach itself to an already formed layer of atoms. Of all the possible attachment sites this is the least desirable, because the only attractions pulling it in come from atoms in this layer. A much better site would be on the surface of one layer of atoms and up against the edge of another partially formed layer sitting on top. In this position the new atom is attracted not only by the atoms in the layer under it, but also by the atoms at the edge of the layer alongside. Such a place is known as a preferred deposition site.

Growth habits and impurities, among other factors, influence crystal form. FACING, FAR LEFT: *Asbestos—fibrous habit.* LEFT: *Sand calcite with impurities.* ABOVE: *Netlike growth habit results in reticulated cerussite.*

a

b

c

d

e

f

Accidents of crystal growth: (a) growth hillocks on diamond crystal; (b) oriented hematite on quartz; (c) striations on anatase; (d) silver dendrite of oriented octahedra;

(e) Japanese twinning in quartz; (f) hopper cube faces on diamond crystal. FACING: *Radiating aggregates of cyanotrichite crystals.*

The presence of a dislocation, or extra row of atoms in the crystal, can force part of the surface up and out of line with the rest, producing what is technically called a screw dislocation. Such a screw dislocation supplies a ready-made preferred deposition site, encouraging the attachment of atoms and accelerating growth. The earmark of such screw dislocation growth is the spiral trace that it leaves on the crystal face in the form of a set of steps.

Line disorders, or dislocations, can exert their influence in a few or many directions in the disordered structure. In some cases such dislocations are uniformly distributed in all directions and growth proceeds with ease in all three dimensions. Some crystals with dislocations encouraging growth in only two dimensions tend to grow as flat plates. Some crystals develop dislocations encouraging growth in only one dimension and thus have little encouragement to grow in width and thickness. They are called whisker crystals and grow rapidly in length—often hundreds of times longer than they are thick.

Disorder in three dimensions would mean that atoms were out of position in all directions. *Three-dimensional disorder* is another way of saying that the material may appear to be solid but does not meet the requirement of an orderly internal structure. The description of glass, given earlier, offers a perfect example of such disorder.

Because of all the many internal stresses and strains, it is a wonder that crystals form at all. When they do form, it is understandable that their appearance will reflect the interplay of conflicting or cooperating internal events. The irregularities in crystal growth are important scientifically because of the clues they give to the secrets of crystal growth. And for the hobbyist and collector they add considerably to the beauty or

oddity of crystal specimens they have acquired.

Along with all their other difficulties in growing, crystals have a tendency to become malformed and to deviate in shape from a textbook ideal. If the malformation expresses itself in a failure to form recognizable, flat crystal faces—even when there is good internal structure—the crystal is said to be anhedral, *an* meaning not and *hedral* meaning formed. Should the crystal have faces that are poorly formed, it is subhedral—less than formed. If the faces are excellent the crystal is euhedral, *eu* meaning well.

The whole problem of malformation arises because something has favored the development of one group of faces and not another. One of the known causes is a steady flowing movement of the solution while the crystals are forming. As the solution flows through the crystal-lined vein or cavity, all the crystal parts facing into the flow receive a fresh supply of building materials and grow rapidly. Those parts in the lee receive only the material that eddies around to them behind the crystal. Although they also grow, it is a slower process.

We must remember that even when the crystals are badly formed, there is an underlying organization. The crystal structure stays the same. All the crystal faces, be they too large or too small, are still at the same angles to each other, and Steno's old Law of Interfacial Angles remains valid.

Miscellaneous designs and figures, standing out in very low relief on an otherwise perfectly smooth and glassy crystal face, are called growth hillocks or growth figures. Sometimes these appear as flat planes or shallow curved surfaces jutting out at very slight angles from the face and covering a considerable portion of it. In such cases they are called vicinal faces.

Many of the better-defined hillocks seem to come from the spiral growth resulting from screw dislocations. When two such dislocations of opposing direction are near neighbors, their respective growth plateaus sweep outward and eventually meet, creating a single plateau which continues to grow toward the edges of the crystal. Since the opposing dislocations are still there, their spiral growth continues to sweep on around, creating a new cycle on a new plateau on top of the original. This continues, plateau upon plateau, until a small hillock is built. If crystal growth is arrested before this pile of tiny plateaus can grow sideward toward the edges of the crystal, it remains as a small, isolated projection—a little hillock—on the main crystal face.

Sometimes the forms of the hillocks show no particularly definite outline. At other times the geometrical outlines they do assume are good evidence of the internal structure of the crystal. Because of this, a rough, broken crystal fragment with at least one good face showing growth figures can often be identified, and the direction of its structural planes determined, without recourse to X-ray techniques. The growth hillocks on crystal faces sometimes continue their growth and become larger single crystals in their own right. Since these hillocks have begun as structural continuations of the parent crystal, this development remains perfectly lined up with the structure of the original crystal. Thus when the parent crystal is rotated under a light, all the related faces of all the individual crystals grown from the various hillocks will flash their reflections in unison. Because all the parts are parallel to each other, this is called a parallel overgrowth.

Parallelism of this kind can also be caused by certain kinds of coatings on a crystal during its growth. A parent crystal may stop growing and become coated with clay, or hematite, or some other mineral. When this coating is thin at certain spots, the original crystal may begin to grow again. Growth is arrested elsewhere by the thicker coating, but each thinly covered spot grows a new crystal portion parallel to each of the others, because all are actually continuations of the crystal's original structure.

There is another striking kind of parallel overgrowth that consists of a crystal knob growing on the end of another crystal, so that it resembles a king's scepter. Quartz supplies the best examples of this scepter growth which, for some unknown reason, limits itself to one large individual growth rather than producing a number of small ones—

More crystal growth accidents. FACING: *Hoppers of halite —salt—from California.* TOP: *Parallel crystals of galena from Joplin, Missouri.* ABOVE: *Curved stacks of chlorite crystals as drawn in* Corso di Mineralogia *(1862).*

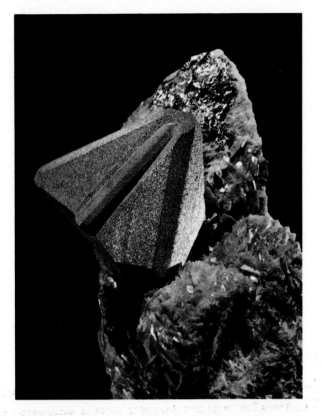

and that one only at one end of the parent crystal.

The concept of an un-growing crystal has an Alice-in-Wonderland sound. Nevertheless, the process that added atoms to the structure as they lost some of their energy can be put in reverse when energy is added to the atoms that are already part of the structure. This is called dissolution, or the return of atoms to solution, and it actually is a process of un-growing that occurs in nature. It starts at random spots on a crystal face and spreads from each spot, gradually leaving a series of small, shallow areas called etch pits. If this etching process is carried on long enough, the entire crystal will go. If arrested, however, the pits can be studied as evidence of crystal structure. Just as crystal growth is precisely controlled by its structure, so is etching.

In nature the etching process starts when the environment that gave birth to the crystal changes to conditions under which the crystal cannot exist. Sometimes, as the crystal starts to go, there are so many tiny etch pits that to the naked eye the crystal face may look frosted, or as if grinding has removed its shiny surface. Magnification, however, will reveal the myriad tiny pits, and show that each of them has the normal triangular, rectangular, or other geometric outline typical of the crystal structure.

There are a number of minerals that occur in curved, twisted, or bent crystals. The causes for this kind of growth have not been completely determined. Whatever the reasons, the crystals themselves are unusual because they introduce curved surfaces into a world of flat planes and geometric figures with measurable angles. The Swiss *strahlers*, who are professional crystal collectors, are always searching for *gwendeln*—twisted crystals of a smoky-colored quartz, found in Alpine veins among more normal quartz and other fine mineral specimens. These twisted quartz crystals are actually a series of flattened quartz crystals stacked up on their sides, each one slightly turned from its neighbor. Sometimes the individuals in the stack are so small that when seen together with the naked eye the whole looks like a single curved crystal.

Dolomite crystals are often stacked together in little groups—again with each crystal slightly turned—that look like small, cream-colored saddles. Stranger still are some crystals of mimetite, especially a yellow to orange-brown variety called campylite, which occurs in England. Many of these individual hexagonal crystals are shaped so that they resemble tiny barrels with both ends flat and with curved edges swelling out at the crystals' middle.

Strangest of all are tiny crystals of a mineral

Three excellent crystal samples of their species. 57

FACING: *Twinned tetrahedrite with chalcopyrite, from Harz
Mountains, Germany.* TOP: *Wulfenite from Chihuahua, Mexico.*
ABOVE: *Celestite from Chittenango Falls, New York.*

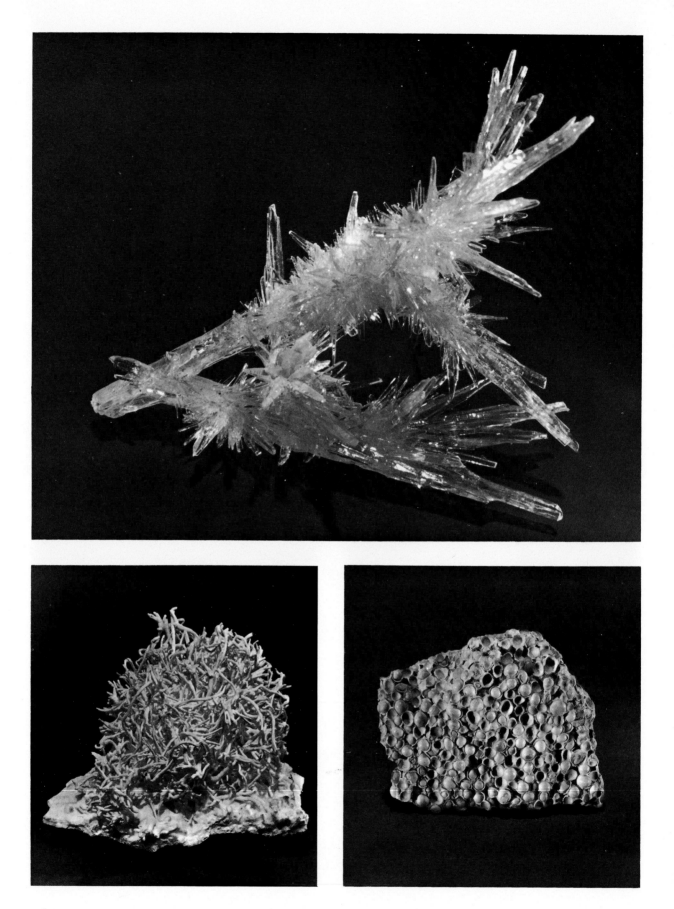

called heteromorphite, from Rumania. Normally this mineral, a compound of lead, antimony and sulfur ($Pb_7Sb_8S_{19}$), occurs in long, shiny, metallic, hairlike crystals. Now and then, however, a few appear that resemble platinum wedding rings. They are completely circular, and almost the color of platinum.

Crystals of a single mineral species are the product of only part of the activity that has occurred within their parent solutions or melts. These solutions and melts also contain atoms of other elements waiting for the proper change in conditions so that they, too, can form crystals. When they do finally crystallize, there is a good possibility they will settle themselves on the crystals that have already formed. Thus they become coatings of one kind or another.

Some coatings are very selective about the sites upon which they will deposit themselves. In the quarries around Paterson and Prospect Park, New Jersey, quartz crystals are found with normal six-sided pyramid terminations. Some of these are coated with a bright red hematite film. Oddly, all six faces are not coated—only alternate ones—creating a gay pinwheel effect. The hematite has recognized that the structure underlying three of the faces is compatible with its own structure, whereas that under the other three is not, and has selected accordingly. The six-sided pyramid is not as simple a structure as it seems to be on first reflection.

Sometimes when one mineral is deposited as a coating on another, its crystals are big enough to be seen as separate entities. Surprisingly, they may be perfectly lined up in one definite structural direction of the crystal host. Although the structures of the two minerals are not alike and cannot form solid solutions, they must have some-

Growth Habits of Single Crystals

Barrel-shaped

Bladed

Capillary

Blocky

Foliated

Tabular

Pyramidal

Stubby

Columnar

In different colonies, aragonite appears to be three different minerals. FACING, TOP: *Acicular aragonite from Utah.* FAR LEFT: *Coralloidal aragonite, Styria, Austria.* LEFT: *Pisolitic aragonite from Bohemia, Czechoslovakia.* ABOVE: *A sampling of shapes—growth habits—of single crystals.*

thing in common. The outer layer of the host crystal is enough like some atom layer in the overgrowth species to confuse the overgrowth into accepting the host layer as one of its own. The overgrowth crystal then proceeds to build its own structure. Perfect examples of this are red rutile crystals, which grow in a flat, netlike pattern on black hematite plates; gold-colored chalcopyrite crystals, which look like thousands of tiny pyramids lined up on the surface of red-brown sphalerite crystals; and tiny bright blue pseudoboleite crystals, which stack like small boxes, one each on the six faces of a cube of blue boleite. Coatings like these are known as oriented crystal overgrowths.

Nature often produces what is called phantom crystals. These are ghostly, crystal-outline images appearing inside a transparent, glassy crystal. The phantoms are only the remnants of crystal coatings that occurred during earlier growth stages. Often, as a crystal forms, its growth stops long enough for the surface to become coated with a variety of mineral substances. If this coating is too heavy, growth stops completely. If, however, the coating is only a light dusting, the crystal can begin to grow again when material is available and conditions are right. This traps the coating in the new growth, a process that can repeat itself again and again so that multiple phantoms, one inside the other, may be formed.

Conditions under which a crystal is growing may become so unfavorable that there is often some question about whether the process will continue. In such a case, growth will most likely proceed along all the edges of the crystal and not on its faces. This produces a kind of skeletal, open-network crystal with all edges and no faces. Such crystals are called hoppers.

There are various reasons for this kind of growth behavior. One has to do with the fact that when an atom joins a crystal structure it gives off its excess energy. This energy must be removed from the crystal before other atoms can be deposited. Physicists have demonstrated that energy leaks off best from objects at sharp points or edges. That is why lightning rods are usually pointed. Since energy leaks off best from crystal edges, rather than faces, edges become the best areas for continued crystal growth. Whatever the explanation, the fact is that whenever growth on the faces of a crystal is suppressed it often continues along the edges, thereby producing these skeletal hoppers.

When rotated on a symmetry axis, a cube of pyrite at first seems to show a fourfold repetition of identical faces as a true cube should. This is very high symmetry and is obvious for true cubes, but a pyrite cube is deceptive. A close look at this pyrite cube will reveal that each face is covered with hundreds of parallel ridges or channels, which run in different directions on different faces. These are called striations, or striae.

These striae are the result of a battle between two different crystal faces, the cube and the pyritohedron, trying to form in the same place at the same time—a process called oscillatory growth. As each battling face momentarily dominates the growth cycle, it leaves a little flat strip of face running in its own direction, only to be cut off by a flat strip running at a different angle. In the example discussed here, the cube has ultimately dominated, so that the crystal looks pretty much like a true cube, except that the grooves on its faces run in different directions on neighboring faces. Rotation of this crystal will not give four identical repetitions because the striations do not

FACING, TOP: *In sedimentary agate from Arizona, crystals are fine-grained, undetectable; impurities suggest a sunset scene.* LEFT: *Igneous dark red almandine garnet from Spruce Pine, North Carolina; crystals are walnut-size.*

match directions. It has no fourfold symmetry.

Pyrite has a different symmetry, then, from a mineral like fluorite, whose cubes always show four exact repetitions when rotated. The presence of striations on crystals, therefore, helps to determine the correct symmetry for pyrite as well as many other minerals.

While it is not a constant characteristic, each mineral tends to form in crystals of a particular shape. For instance, fluorite crystals can occur with different sets of faces—the cube, octahedron, dodecahedron, and several others. Almost always, however, they occur as cubes. The habit, or usual shape, for fluorite, then, is the cube. This means that the fluorite structure favors a process of growth producing cube faces.

Strangely enough, crystals end up favoring the faces that grow most slowly. The cube faces, for example, are the kind that grow slowest in fluorite. This situation can be disrupted and crystal habit can be changed by the introduction of impurities. The impurities tend to congregate on the faces where most of the growth activity is found. They interfere with the growth of these faces, slow them down, and give them a chance to compete with the slowest-growing crystal faces, which usually dominate the final shape of the crystal.

Some of the more easily recognized overall shapes, or growth habits, of crystals are illustrated on page 59.

Acicular: From a Latin word meaning needle, this refers to crystals that are long and thin, like those found in the species natrolite and mesolite.

Barrel-Shaped: Self-descriptive term applied to such crystals as vanadinite and mimetite.

Bladed: Crystals that are flat, broad, and long, like a knife blade, are so described. Kyanite and hemimorphite are good examples.

Blocky: This describes the appearance of crystals that are almost of equal dimension in all directions and look like children's toy blocks. Some of the feldspars, galena, and fluorite can be so described.

Columnar: These crystals are thick and fairly elongated, shaped in miniature like the columns of a building. Examples include beryl, quartz, and tourmaline. Sometimes the word *prismatic* is used to describe the same crystals, because the dominant faces on columnar crystals are usually called prisms.

Capillary: From a Latin word meaning hair,

62

Native gold occurs fairly often in branchlike dendritic groups, like this handsome gold dendrite from Transylvania, Rumania. The color can vary considerably, generally depending on the amount of silver present.

capillary is often used interchangeably with *fili-form*, also from the Latin, and means thread-shaped. The terms describe minerals such as silver, which is sometimes found as thin wires, or miller-ite, which is found in long, very thin, stiff wires.

Pyramidal: This expression is used when the ends, or even the entire crystal, look vaguely like three-, four-, or six-sided pyramids. Examples include wulfenite and anatase.

Stubby: Such crystals are also sometimes de-scribed as *stout* or *equant*. All three terms try to draw an image of crystals that are neither flattened nor elongated, but are nearly the same dimensions in all directions. Tourmaline, apatite, and beryl can be columnar or prismatic, but they may also be of shorter lengths and stubby.

Tabular: This means that the crystal's growth has been flat, with only minor thickness. Wulfenite is often tabular, rather than pyramidal, and tor-bernite is almost always tabular.

Crystals seem to prefer to collect in groups. Sometimes they have little choice, but the result is that an isolated, single crystal is a relatively rare thing in nature. Most rocks and minerals of the almond, this refers to almond-shaped cavities that are commonly found in volcanic rocks. These cavities were originally the same spherical shape as the gas bubbles that formed them, but the flow of the rock flattened and stretched them. Often they are filled with collections of minerals, phillipsite, analcime, heulandite or others, which then become known as amygdaloidal minerals.

Bladed: Individual crystal blades are sometimes massed together in aggregates, so that the term can be used to describe either the separate crystals or the group.

Colloform: There is a tendency to use this term to replace several others that mean roughly the same thing. All colloform aggregates are partially spherical or rounded on the outside. Botryoidal, from the Greek, means that the aggregate looks like a cluster of grapes. Mammillary, from the Latin, means that it looks rounded, like a breast. Reniform, from the Latin for kidney, again refers to a roughly rounded form. Globular is self-explanatory, describing a rounded shape.

None of these expressions refers to the shape of individual crystals in the group, but only to its total rounded form. Malachite, hematite, and wavellite all seem to grow from a number of acicular or needle-shaped crystals deposited on a surface. As they continue to grow, those that push outward from the surface have access to fresh material and continue their growth, while those lying in other directions remain stunted and are eventually covered up by the rest. Thus the aggregate becomes a group of thickening needles pushing out from the surface, and eventually growing together to form a mass with a rounded surface composed of the ends of the crystals. The term colloform is used because it is believed that most crystal aggregates of this

earth's crust are in aggregates of individuals that are anhedral—with no distinguishable crystal faces. These aggregates vary from those so tiny that they are just visible under a good optical microscope to those so large that individual crystals in the group are several feet long. Almost always the arrangement of crystals in the aggregates is haphazard. Only rarely are they oriented toward each other in some particular way.

In the early days of mineralogy, differences in the kinds of crystal groupings were given undue importance. Some minerals were even divided into several species because their crystals looked different in different groupings. Following are some of the most easily recognized crystal groupings:

Arborescent: These are treelike groups, with the crystals in branching, perhaps fernlike, arrangements. These are sometimes called *dendrite* groups from the Greek word for tree. More species tend to crystallize as dendrites than in any other way. Natural gold, silver, and copper crystals generally form this way. Pyrolusite and psilomelane, two oxides of manganese in dendrites, account for the beautiful black, fernlike staining that appears in many sedimentary rocks.

Amygdaloidal: From a Greek word meaning

ABOVE: *From Collier County, Kansas, delicate dendrites of manganese oxide supported by and preserved in agate—called moss agate because of the mossy patterns created by the impurities.* FACING: *This sampling of crystal colonies shows the shapes in which particular minerals characteristically congregate.*

Crystal Colonies
Growth Habits of Groups of Crystals

Pisolitic: Bauxite

Columnar: Arsenopyrite

Banded: Agate

Dendritic: Psilomelane

Stalactitic: Limonite

Divergent, bladed: Hemimorphite

Fibrous, massive: Asbestos

Arborescent: Copper

Radiated, globular: Wavellite

Granular: Olivine

Concentric: Malachite

Plumose: Muscovite

Massive: Clay

Micaceous: Mica

kind grow from gelatin-like accumulations of the mineral material. These are called colloids, from a Greek word meaning glue.

Compact or massive: These terms refer to small, interlocked crystals closely packed, so that they do not appear to be crystallized at all. Some of the clay minerals are good examples of this kind of grouping.

Cockscomb: Flat, fanlike arrangements of crystals, with their pointed ends giving a sawtooth effect, are commonly found in the mineral species marcasite.

Coralloidal: The twisted, tangled, cylindrical growth of aragonite, which makes it look like a mass of white coral, gave rise to this term.

Drusy: A mineral or rock surface coated with a layer of fairly uniform crystals of small size is called a druse.

Earthy: A mass that crumbles like dried mud and seems to have no crystalline character is earthy.

Fibrous: Asbestos is a typical fibrous mineral. It consists of very compact bundles of long,

fibrous, almost silky crystals. It is usually easy to strip off small groups of silky hairs from a fibrous mass.

Granular: This refers to a mass made of small individual crystal grains.

Micaceous: This word describes the characteristic of mica minerals that permits them to be split off easily in very thin sheets. Sometimes *lamellar*, from the Latin meaning plate or layer, and *foliated*, from the Latin meaning leaf, are used to describe the same characteristic.

Nodular: The term is used to describe lumps or kernels or nodules of the mineral, but does not indicate whether the object in question is a single crystal fragment or a multiple crystalline mass.

Oolitic, Pisolitic: Both of these terms are used for small, concentric, globular masses of mineral. Oolitic is used for globules about the size of fish eggs, and pisolitic for objects as big as peas. Anything larger is usually just called a concretion.

Plumose: Sometimes the mica minerals and their near relatives form in scaly, spreading accumulations that resemble feathery plumes.

Radiated, divergent: The crystals in this group start growing at some central spot and spread outward. If they separate from each other enough to be distinguished individually, they are divergent.

Reticulated: This word comes from the Latin and means net. It refers to the open lattice made by numerous crossed bars of some crystallized minerals. Reticulated cerussite and reticulated rutile are the best examples.

Rosette: Any large mineral collection contains at least one example of Swiss *Eisenrose*—literally, iron rose. This is a crystal group of flat, shiny

FACING: *Cuprite, a red copper oxide, sometimes occurs in whisker crystals, which are really grossly elongated cubes.* ABOVE: *Native copper from Lake Michigan's great Keeweenaw Peninsula deposits.*

hematite crystals arranged in an overlapping pattern around a center—just as are the petals of a rose.

Specular: This word originally derives from the Latin word *speculum*, or mirror. In mineralogical terms it means that something is as bright and shiny as a mirror. A specimen of specular hematite is one with many tiny, brilliant crystal plates.

Stalactitic: The Greek origin of this word refers to the oozing out of drops necessary to produce cave formations known as stalactites. Any deposit of mineral material formed by the same process—such as malachite, aragonite, goethite, or calcite—is said to be stalactitic.

Ordinarily crystal aggregates are accidentally arranged, or at best organized in a crude way. There are many groups, however, of two or more crystals that are joined to each other as are Siamese twins, sharing the same structures. These twins start to form early in crystal growth when some of the atoms, instead of occupying proper lattice positions, find themselves in other positions which the energy of the lattice permits but does not prefer. These atoms get there because of the mixups that occur during rapid crystallization. Once there, they form a kind of nucleus from which crystal growth continues. The two segments then continue to grow side by side, quite compatible because they are structurally comfortable together. The plane at which the two parts of the twin join is called the composition plane. Usually it is not difficult to see where twins join, because at that intersection the crystal faces meet in V-shaped junctions. These are technically known as reentrant angles because the V's point into the body of the crystal.

Since there are few structural positions that are permitted to the misplaced atom, there are very few angles at which the twins can form. Each known angle is called a twin law. As an example, the mineral staurolite is often found in a twin formation in which the two related parts penetrate each other at right angles to make a cross. They are often sold to tourists in Virginia and elsewhere as "fairy crosses." This right-angle twin is one of two possibilities for staurolite. Its other twin law permits the crystals to penetrate at about 60 degrees, rather than 90 degrees. For other minerals there are Brazil twins, butterfly twins, Dauphine twins, spinel twins, fishtail twins, bishop's miter twins.

There are several fundamental kinds of twinning. Twinning with two individuals in contact with each other as if they had been glued together is appropriately called contact twinning. The staurolite twins mentioned above are called penetration twins, because they look as if one of the crystals had been forced through the other and out the opposite side. Sometimes the contact or penetration twins continue in a circle until a wheel-shaped group is produced. These are called cyclic twins. At other times the twinning is repeated back and forth a great number of times in a row, so that individual twin segments cannot be easily distinguished. Under magnification, however, it can be seen that the structure is zigzagging back and forth. This is called polysynthetic twinning; it is very common with certain feldspar minerals, such as albite.

For the crystallographer, twinning confuses and complicates the study of crystal symmetry, since it often makes crystals appear to be more symmetrical than they really are. For the mineral collector, on the other hand, the phenomenon produces a great number of geometrically interesting and sometimes beautiful objects.

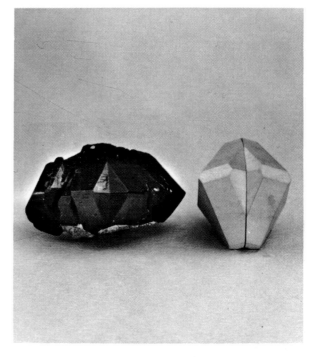

All statements, definitions, and discussions of crystals are rather firm in their insistence on an organized structure. Strangely enough, there are some true crystals that have no organized structure. Perhaps it would be better to say that they had structure at one time, but that it has become thoroughly disordered. Minerals of this kind have metamict crystals. Interestingly, they are always radioactive, containing less than 1 percent of uranium or thorium atoms. This is the direct cause of their strange condition. The original structures, through long periods of radioactive bombardment from the uranium and thorium, literally have been battered into disorder.

It is quite possible to reproduce this metamict condition in the laboratory. The crystals retain the general outward appearance and the same chemical analysis. However, they lose their characteristics of cleavage, behavior with light, reaction to X-rays, and all others that depend on

structure. When metamict crystals are heated, giving the atoms a new freedom of movement, they regain their crystalline characteristics and give off so much heat that they become incandescent and glow brightly. When we remember that organizing (or reorganizing) a crystal structure means a release of energy for all the atoms, we can understand where the heat comes from.

Crystals develop in so many different ways, and are subject to so many vagaries of growth, that the English writer John Ruskin was moved to write of them, "They are wonderfully like human creatures . . . never think what is to happen tomorrow. . . . You will see crowds of them forced to constitute themselves in a hurry. . . . Then you will find indulged crystals who have changed their minds and ways continually . . . been tired, and taken heart . . . been sick, and got well . . . thought they would try a different diet, and then thought better of it; and made but a poor use of their advantages, after all."

ABOVE: *Tetragonal rutile crystal from Brazil is so malformed by twinning that it resembles the orthorhombic model beside it.* FAR RIGHT: *Twinned cassiterite from Bohemia and model—both orthorhombic.*

Gemstones: the Royal Line

3

Mineral specimens are often magnificent—but they are no match for the glamour of great gems

Before the dawn of history men were finding and assigning special values to certain kinds of rock and mineral pebbles that were rare or particularly beautiful. Thus was born the gemstone: a mineral set apart from the rest by beauty, rareness, and durability. The combination of attributes is relatively uncommon. Perhaps only one hundred mineral species are considered gems. For the sake of these baubles, wars have been fought, kingdoms have changed hands, and assassinations have been committed.

Gemstone lore, legend, and superstition have been part of every human society. In almost every culture gem materials have been given religious or spiritual significance. The signs of the zodiac, for example, have been associated in several religions with gemstones that traditionally helped them to exercise their influence over mortals.

At the beginning of the fifth century, St. Jerome spoke of a relationship between the twelve gemstones in the breastplate of the Jewish High Priest, the twelve months of the year, and the twelve signs of the zodiac. However, the custom of wearing a birth-month stone is not ancient; it does not seem to have developed until the eighteenth century in Poland, and is perpetuated to this day in the official birthstone list of the jewelry industry: for January, garnet; February, amethyst; March, aquamarine or bloodstone;

April, diamond; May, emerald; June, moonstone or pearl; July, ruby; August, peridot or sardonyx; September, sapphire; October, opal or tourmaline; November, topaz or citrine; December, turquoise or lapis lazuli.

The occult powers of gems may be very much open to question, but they have—besides their beauty and durability—a concrete characteristic that makes them highly desirable. Gems combine high value with small size. They are easy to transport, easy to conceal, and easily convertible to money. In times of stress, when the value of money has weakened, gems have often been the means of saving the substance of an estate. Real-estate holdings may not survive a revolution, but a secret hoard of gems may outlast any political system.

With expanding populations and increasing prosperity in several countries of the world, the number of potential customers for gems—as for paintings and other works of art—is increasing far more rapidly than the available supply. Result: a vast annual trade, and rising prices. Unfortunately for the buying public, it generally does not know much about gemstones.

It is not essential for the gem buyer to master truly technical information. But there are certain basic facts that can be easily assimilated and can reinforce him with a certain amount of knowledge even though he must still rely on the jeweler in technical matters. Certain essential characteristics, italicized below, must always be reviewed when the quality and value of a gemstone are under consideration.

The *hardness* of a gem is the resistance it gives to scratching and general wear. Mohs' Scale, a rough scale of hardness used for all minerals, is the convenient and generally accepted guide.

PRECEDING PAGES: *Rough gem material must be expertly analyzed to determine how best it can be converted into marketable gems. Leading diamond-cutters like Bernard de Haan work only on diamond rough.*

All gemstones of any importance have a hardness above 6 in this scale. If less than 6 in hardness, they are not durable enough for use as gems. Any gem material that is not scratched by a sample of quartz, but is by topaz, would have a hardness of 7.5. For testing purposes, to help identify a gemstone by its hardness, the jeweler may use a set of pencil-like tools with hardness points made of minerals in the scale.

The *weight* of gemstones is usually given in carats, one carat equaling one-fifth of a gram. Converting this into more familiar units, there are about 140 carats in an ounce. Even knowing that the carat is an expression of weight and not size, gem buyers are always surprised to see that a 1-carat sapphire is considerably smaller than a 1-carat diamond. Sapphire is denser than diamond and a smaller stone can therefore weigh the same number of carats as a larger diamond.

Determining the *specific gravity* of a gem involves two measurements at the same time—size and weight. We are aware of a difference in weight when we compare iron and wood, yet it would not always be correct to say that iron weighs more than wood since a large piece of

TOP: *Woodcut of a lapidary shop from the medieval medical work* Hortus Sanitatis: *stones, like plants, were thought to have curative properties.* RIGHT: *A Renaissance classic, Leonardus' celebrated gem book appeared in English in 1750.*

wood can weigh more than a small piece of iron. Only by comparing equal volumes of these materials can the extent of the weight difference be clear and unmistakable. Diamond is three and one-half times heavier than an equal volume of water—normally used as the standard of measurement—hence its specific gravity is 3.5.

The ability of mineral structures to bend a beam of light can easily be demonstrated (see page 113). The amount of bending or refraction—the mineral's *index of refraction*—depends entirely on the species of mineral involved, because it is an effect brought about by the mineral's structure. The degree of bending, measured by a refractometer, is useful in gem identification, since every gem has a different index of refraction.

When Newton split a beam of white light into its various wavelengths, or colors, he demonstrated the phenomenon of *dispersion*. The amount of refraction when a beam of light strikes a gemstone depends not only on the gem's structure, but also upon the wavelength of the light. The blue wavelength, for example, is bent more than the red. Since white light is composed of all wavelengths, each tends to be bent a different amount and the light is thus separated and sorted into a rainbow of colors. If the gemstone has strong dispersive ability, like diamond, it will cause a wider separation of the wavelengths and sparkle with colored flashes whenever struck by a beam of white light.

Chatoyancy—from the French meaning cat's eye—refers to the single slit of light, like the contracted pupil of a cat's eye, reflected from certain rounded, oval-cut gemstones. Closely related is the *asterism*, or starlike reflection, so well known in star rubies and star sapphires.

These effects are the results of inclusions—

FACING: *Goldwork in the Celtic-German tradition on the ninth-century* Lindau Gospels; *light filters through jewels in raised mountings.* ABOVE: *Five-inch beryl crystals from Brazil, rare because still attached to albite feldspar.*

75

foreign bodies—found in some mineral crystals. Generally inclusions are considered undesirable in gemstones except as an aid in identification. However, some inclusions can greatly enhance the value and beauty of a gem by producing striking light effects.

Chatoyant mineral specimens contain inclusions of needle-shaped reflecting bodies of other species, such as rutile. These inclusions may even be hollow tubes. A combined reflection phenomenon—chatoyancy—is produced when the tubes or needles are oriented in parallel bundles. By cutting the gemstones as oval or circular domes, the gem cutter is able to reveal the resemblance to a cat's eye.

Asterism is an effect that can occur when there are several sets of needle inclusions. In crystals of corundum—from which we get the gemstones ruby and sapphire—these sets arrange themselves in three different directions, 120 degrees apart, parallel to possible crystal faces. Instead of one band of light there are now three bands, intersecting at a common point. If the gem is properly cut the effect is a reflection of a bright star of light.

GEMSTONES: Armed with these brief explanations, we can now look more closely at individual gem species. The list is by no means exhaustive; it is compiled from personal preferences.

Diamond: Diamond, a naturally occurring variety of carbon, is not only "a girl's best friend" but a jeweler's as well; it is the backbone of his trade. Through historical accident, its own fine characteristics, and effective promotion, it is now at least as highly treasured as it was in the past.

Its value and its rarity have always been legendary. An ancient story attributed to Aristotle says,

"No one except Alexander ever reached the place where the diamond is produced. This is a valley connected with the land of Hind. The glance cannot penetrate to its greatest depths and serpents are found there, the like of which no man hath seen, and upon which no man can gaze without dying. However, this power endures only as long as the serpents live, for when they die the power leaves them. In this place summer reigns for six months and winter for the same length of time. Now, Alexander ordered that an iron mirror should be brought and placed at the spot where the serpents dwelt. When the serpents approached, their glance fell upon their own image in the mirror and this caused their death. Hereupon, Alexander wished to bring out the diamonds from the valley, but no one was willing to undertake the descent. Alexander therefore sought council of the wise men, and they told him to throw down a piece of flesh into the valley. This he did, the diamonds became attached to the flesh, and

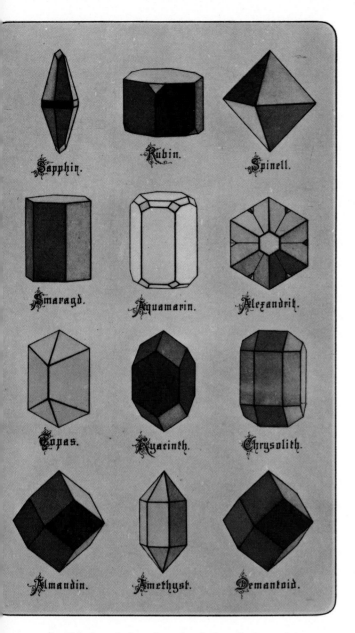

Sapphir. Rubin. Spinell.

Smaragd. Aquamarin. Alexandrit.

Topas. Kyacinth. Chrysolith.

Almandin. Amethyst. Demantoid.

that this diamond was only part of an original crystal twice the size. It was bought by the government of Transvaal and given to King Edward VII of England in 1907. The great rough stone was then cut. From it came the Star of Africa, 530.2 carats, the largest cut diamond in the world, now set in the King's Royal Scepter. In addition, the mass provided a 317.4-carat gem now set in the Imperial State Crown; two large stones of 94.45 and 63.65 carats, which are set in the Queen's Crown, where the Kohinoor, another fabulous find, is also displayed; five stones weighing 18.85, 11.51, 8.8, 6.8, and 4.4 carats; ninety-six additional stones weighing 7.55 carats in all. Other sensational discoveries have occurred with some regularity for centuries.

The Kohinoor itself has a history lost in antiquity. This diamond, which weighs 108.9 carats in its present cut form, first officially appeared in 1304, when it came into the hands of the Mogul emperors of India. Legend, however, traces it back almost five thousand years.

Large diamonds like the Cullinan and the Kohinoor easily catch the public fancy. However, these stones are commercially insignificant compared to the wealth of smaller diamonds required for the gem trade and for industrial uses. Diamond mining that relies on predatory birds, as in Alexander's method, makes a romantic legend. It is questionable whether even Alexander ever really tried it. In any case, modern, practical methods for mining diamonds require earth-moving machinery and other processing equipment.

Even considering the more than three-ton total of gem and commercial diamond mined each year, diamond is a rare mineral. In the rich South African mines, it is found only as one part in fourteen million of the ore. This partially accounts

the birds of the air seized the flesh and bore it up out of the valley. Then Alexander ordered his people to pursue the birds and to pick up what fell from the flesh."

The most fantastic diamond ever found weighed more than one and one-third pounds before it was cut. It was the Cullinan diamond, named for Sir Thomas Cullinan, chairman of the Transvaal Company at whose Premier Mine in South Africa the stone was found in 1905. Its shape suggested

FACING: *Jewels like these garnet-set gold Etruscan earrings, c. 200 B.C., are valuable archaeological clues.*
ABOVE: *From the rare* Grundriss der Edelsteinkunde *(1887), a group of mineral crystals, precisely drawn.*

for the nearly constant price of diamond, which is almost as high as that of the most expensive gems in the world, rubies and emeralds. And in spite of this price, the demand for diamond remains so great that operating producers and freelance prospectors are always out searching for more.

Historically, the earliest known diamonds came from river gravels in India and Borneo. The Golconda district in India was one of the first regular producers. India's other important diamond districts are one farther north, between the Mahanadi and Godavari Rivers, and one in central India, near the city of Panna. From ancient times until the discovery of diamonds in Brazil in 1728, these Indian mines were major producers. Now their yield is so small that profits barely justify costs.

Diamond mining in Brazil began when slaves looking for gold found some unusual, bright, shiny pebbles. When these were identified as diamonds, the rush began. Diamond mines opened at the headwaters of Rio Jequitinhonha in Minas Gerais and of Rio San Francisco in Bahia. Here, as in India, the diamonds were found in the washed river gravels. It was the custom that when a slave found a particularly fine stone, he was honored, fitted out with new clothes, and given his freedom. One local legend tells of the woman slave who found the 254-carat Star of the South; she was not only freed, but pensioned for life.

The Brazilian diamond mining industry was eclipsed in the 1800s when rich diamond deposits were discovered in South Africa. Brazilian mining methods were primitive, accessible ore fields had been mined out, and the deposits could not produce as bountifully as those of Africa. There was a succession of diamond strikes on the African

continent, starting with the great South African rush of 1866. And still the intensive search for diamonds continues.

A diamond is often called the "king of gems." Composed of almost pure carbon, it has to a high degree everything a mineral substance requires to be considered a gemstone—brilliance, beauty, durability, rarity, portability. It also happens to be fashionable—an added advantage. Because of its high index of refraction and high dispersion it produces brilliant flashes of bright colored fire. Its durability is beyond question, since it is the hardest natural substance known. But hardness is merely a measure of resistance to wear and abrasion; this does not mean that diamonds are unbreakable. Breakage has to do with how well the material holds together. Diamond resists scratching because there is no natural substance hard enough to scratch it. Diamond is brittle, however, and it does have a cleavage— what the diamond-cutters call a grain. Under the shock of a sudden sharp blow a diamond may crack or chip or even cleave.

Diamond can be found in a wide range of colors. Most gem diamonds are water-clear and

Two specimens still embedded in their matrix materials. FACING: *From Minas Gerais, Brazil, brilliant varicolored tourmaline in lepidolite mica.* ABOVE: *Red crystal sections of ruby embedded in chrome zoicite, from Tanzania.*

colorless. Some have a very pale, steely blue tint, which gives rise to the term blue-white. Color—or lack of it—is important in the commercial grading of diamonds. Two diamonds, alike in their brilliance and the beauty and perfection of their cut, and totally lacking in inclusions, may differ a hundred percent in price because of a subtle difference in color. Really fine colored diamonds, or "fancies," are quite rare and bring premium prices. Yellow and brown colors are commonest, but if only pale in hue they actually reduce the value of the diamond. Greenish diamonds are sometimes found; rarest of all are red, pink, and blue stones.

Considering the rarity of truly blue diamonds, it comes as something of a surprise to see the Hope diamond for the first time in its black felt-lined private vault at the Smithsonian Institution in Washington. It weighs 44.5 carats and is a deep, rich blue. People often compare its color to sapphire, but it really is a dark, hard, indigo blue, very much the same color that you

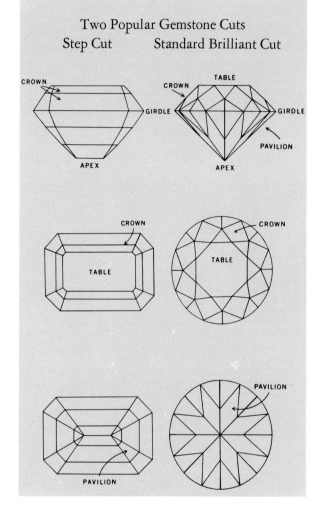

Two Popular Gemstone Cuts
Step Cut   Standard Brilliant Cut

would expect to see on heated steel. The Hope diamond's fantastic history reads like a detective story with inexplicable gaps. It was brought to France from India in 1642 by Tavernier, a noted gem explorer, who sold it to Louis XIV in 1668. After it was cut into a triangular-shaped gem weighing 67.13 carats, it made its way into the collection of French crown jewels. In 1792, during the French Revolution, it was seized and deposited with other treasures at the Garde-Meuble, from which it subsequently disappeared.

In 1830 a blue diamond, somewhat lopsided and weighing 44.5 carats, was sold to Sir Henry Thomas Hope in London. It seemed to be a cut-down piece of the French Blue. In 1874, when the Duke of Brunswick's gems were sold at auction in Geneva, a blue stone weighing between 6 and 7 carats was among them. In color and quality it was astonishingly like the Hope diamond, and very likely was the missing tip of the French Blue.

The Hope itself made its way through several

FACING: *A nineteenth-century artist's conception of a smoky quartz grotto in the Swiss Alps. Such caves led to the old notion that quartz was frozen water.* ABOVE: *Colored stones are often step cut; the many-faceted brilliant cut best displays the fire of such stones as diamonds.*

hands, leaving behind a legendary trail of misfortune and violence, until it was acquired in 1949 by Harry Winston, the New York jeweler, who later presented it to the Smithsonian.

With diamonds so rare, so intriguing, and so much in demand, it is inevitable that many attempts are made to find or manufacture less expensive substitutes. Some of the substitutes are sufficiently deceptive so that at a short distance it is impossible to tell them from the real thing.

The natural gemstones that most frequently substitute for diamonds are zircon, white sapphire, and white spinel. Synthetic rutile and strontium titanate are also used, as is glass. White sapphire and white spinel can be detected by careful examination because they lack the bright flashes of fire so characteristic of diamond. Strontium titanate, on the other hand, has entirely too much flashing color; it has four times the color-dispersing ability of diamond and looks gaudy by contrast. Synthetic rutile is always a little yellowish, even though it has some of the necessary fire. Rhinestones, at one time cut from quartz but now cut from glass, have no fire, lack brilliance, and, since they are of soft material, often show innumerable scratches under magnification. This leaves zircon as the best substitute because it has clarity of color, sufficient hardness, and brilliant fire. The expert, however, can always identify zircon by examining the edges of the back facets, through the top of the stone, with a magnifier. They appear doubled because zircon is a double-refracting substance. Diamond is not.

The laboratory manufacture of synthetic diamonds has reached the point where a steady production of small commercial-grade stones is possible. Crystals of the size needed for gemstones, however, will have to be taken from nature's storehouse for some time to come.

Ruby aud sapphire: The name ruby comes from the Latin word *ruber*, meaning red. Sapphire is also from the Latin and means blue. It is valid to consider them together because ruby and sapphire are the same mineral species—corundum—which is an oxide of aluminum (Al_2O_3). The red color in ruby is due to traces of chromium replacing a bit of aluminum in solid solution. Sometimes the coloring is more rose than red. It varies through carmine to a dark purplish red called pigeon's blood. Stones of this deep, rich red coloring come from Burma and they are known as Burma rubies.

Rubies of good quality and color are very rare; when such stones exceed a weight of 10 carats they are among the world's rarest gems. Fewer than half a dozen cut rubies have been recorded as important enough and large enough to carry individual names. Two of these are in the United States: the 100-carat De Long ruby at the American Museum of Natural History in New

FACING: *White-tipped amethyst from Guerrero, Mexico.* TOP: *From a recent Panamanian excavation, a thousand-year-old gold and emerald pendant.*
ABOVE: *Gem tourmaline from Minas Gerais, Brazil.*

York, and the 138.7-carat Rosser Reeves ruby at the Smithsonian in Washington. These are possibly the largest and finest star rubies in the world.

Although sapphire means blue, any kind of corundum, except red, has come to be called sapphire. The finest sapphires come from Soomjam, in Kashmir, and are a soft, velvety, cornflower blue, which in the gem trade is called Kashmir blue. Corundum is colorless only when pure; traces of iron, chromium, titanium, and other metals will produce blue, yellow, and gold gems. Sometimes a single stone will show zones of two colors, such as yellow and blue. Unfortunately there has been a tendency to give a different name to each corundum color variation, which confuses identification. Thus we may hear green

sapphire called "oriental emerald" and yellow sapphire called "oriental topaz." Also, because certain other gems, particularly spinel, strongly resemble ruby and sapphire, there is often further mis-identification. Neither the famous Black Prince's "ruby" nor the Timur "ruby" in the British crown jewels, for example, are really rubies. Both are red spinel. The very large "ruby" that King Gustav III of Sweden gave to Catherine the Great of Russia is not a ruby, either. It is a remarkably fine red gem of another mineral, tourmaline.

Corundum is usually opaque and poorly colored, but being the next hardest natural substance to diamond, it is an important commercial abrasive. It is far more plentiful than diamond and can therefore be economically mined for industrial uses. The crystals are hexagonal in symmetry and, although very hard, are somewhat brittle. The specific gravity is about 4.0, which is among the highest for gemstones. This explains why a relatively small gemstone of ruby or sapphire may be several carats in weight.

Good-quality corundum—as indicated above, hard to come by—meets many of the criteria for gemstones. It occurs in transparent stones of several beautiful colors and its hardness enables it to take a high polish, which is extremely durable.

Near Mandalay, Myitkyina, and Mogok, in Burma, ruby and sapphire mines have been in operation for centuries, but the most productive of them, near Mogok, are now being mined only sporadically. From the abundance of artifacts found there it is obvious that they were worked as early as the Stone Age. The stones themselves come mainly from gravels that were weathered out of the underlying metamorphic limestones of the region.

Almost all the other noteworthy occurrences

of ruby and sapphire are in Asia. Ceylon has produced quantities of fine sapphire, second only to Burma, and primitive mining is still carried on in the gravels there. Thailand, from mines near Chantabun, has produced some dark rubies, though it is better known for the sapphires found near Battambang.

One of the interesting earmarks of a ruby or sapphire from an Asian mine is the way it is cut. Most stones are cut at the sites where they are found. Since the natives are paid for the weight of the finished stone, they usually cut with no regard for overall symmetry or beauty, but only to recover the maximum weight from the rough piece. As a result, most of these native-cut stones are peculiarly shaped, with deep bellies on the

backs of the stones. The natives are very clever, too, at cutting parti-colored blue and white stones in such a way that the blue becomes the bottom point. It thus suffuses the entire stone with color.

The gem corundum occurrences outside of Asia are of lesser importance. The best green sapphires come from Australia. In the United States, quantities of small but very fine sapphires of many colors are found at Yogo Gulch in Montana. Small rubies of fair quality have been found at Cowee Creek in Macon County, North Carolina.

Colorful superstitions, which have trailed the ruby and the sapphire from ancient times, have died hard—or not at all. Some Burmese are still convinced that a ruby, embedded in the flesh, will protect its wearer from bodily harm. Among

Three steps in the delicate art of diamond cleaving.
FACING, TOP: *Cleavage is analyzed, marked;* BELOW: *Rough crystal is scored.* ABOVE: *Cleaving. Result can be two or more pieces of fine gem rough—or comparative disaster.*

are still visible—hundreds of mine shafts, some going down eight hundred feet. In them have been found mining tools dating back to 1650 B.C. These mines are dead; but the emerald, after all this time, is still extremely valuable and eagerly sought.

Emerald is a green variety of the mineral species beryl, which exists in many colors and in considerable quantity. The special value of emerald lies in its rich green color, which is very rare. Emerald, and all other beryl, is chemically a beryllium aluminum silicate ($Be_3Al_2Si_6O_{18}$). The various colors are produced by traces of other elements in solid solution. For emerald, the coloring agent is a small amount of chromium. Emerald, with a hardness of 8, is one of the more durable gemstones. It crystallizes in the hexagonal system, often occurring in very well-formed euhedral crystals. Its specific gravity is 2.7, not nearly as high as sapphire, so that stones of large size can be worn without discomfort.

The finest emeralds ever mined have come from mines in Colombia—at Chivor, Muso, and elsewhere—since long before the time of the Spanish conquest. There they occur in veins of calcite in a rather dark-colored, carbon-bearing limestone. A beautiful eight-ounce gem crystal in the British Museum—the Duke of Devonshire emerald—illustrates the unusual size and quality of the Colombian gems.

There are many other occurrences of emerald in the world, in Austria, Brazil, Russia, Australia, South Africa, Southern Rhodesia, India, and Norway. These vary in quality from very poor to very good, but even the best colored stones, such as those from Russia, never attain the size of those from Colombia. The United States has produced large emerald crystals of good color

the Sinhalese the star sapphire is regarded as protection against witchcraft. This may account for the comparative inactivity of witches in the United States, where two of the most magnificent star sapphires in the world are located. They are the 536-carat Star of India in the American Museum of Natural History in New York and the 330-carat Star of Asia in the Smithsonian Institution.

Emerald: More than thirty-five hundred years ago, about one hundred miles north of Aswan, Egypt, on the slopes of Jebel Sikait and Jebel Zubara, feverish mining activity was producing emeralds for most of the jewelry of the ancient world. The so-called Cleopatra's Emerald Mines

FACING: *Early Brazilian diamond mining.* THIS PAGE,

TOP: *Waterkloof, South Africa, 1852—one of many battles lost by local Kaffirs to the British in what later became diamond country.*

ABOVE: *Kimberley diamond market, 1888.*

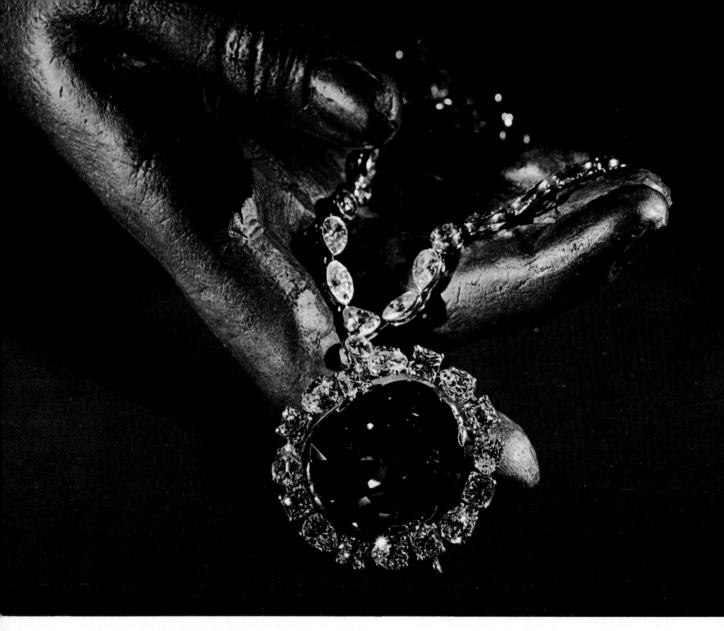

in North Carolina, but because of fractures and inclusions their clarity leaves much to be desired.

By far the bulk of all beryl mined is valuable as a source of the metal beryllium, but useless as a source of gemstones. However, it is not unusual to find crystals that can be cut into superb gems weighing over a thousand carats. One crystal from near the village of Marambaya in Minas Gerais, Brazil, weighed over two hundred pounds. It was laboriously brought to the coast and shipped to the great gem-cutting center at Idar-Oberstein in Germany, where it was cut into 200,000 carats of many small stones. This crystal was an aquamarine, the blue-green variety of beryl caused by solid solution of a small amount of iron. The very deep-blue gemstone aquamarine, seen in jewelry stores, is always produced artificially, by heating greenish or certain yellow-brown crystals to a temperature of 800 degrees Fahrenheit. The resultant color change is permanent.

Aquamarine and the other non-emerald beryls are found in pegmatites. Their large, well-formed crystals are typical of pegmatite minerals. Emeralds, found in metamorphic rocks, have crystallized under much more difficult circumstances and therefore are not as well formed.

Best known among modern sites for gem beryl

are the prospects near Teofilio Otoni and Minas Novas in the state of Minas Gerais, Brazil. Good stones have also come from the Malagasy Republic (or Madagascar), from the Ural Mountains and Transbaikalia in Russia, and from the United States, chiefly from New England and California.

There have been numerous and fairly successful attempts to find substitutes and imitations for natural beryl gemstones. The most successful synthetic emerald is the Chatham emerald, named for its originator. This is a beautiful gemstone with the appearance of high-quality emerald. Usually the stones are small and, although considerably less costly than natural stones of the same quality, are still fairly expensive.

A synthetic blue spinel is easily made and can be successfully substituted for a rich blue aquamarine. The "soude" emerald is also a successful substitute, although it is easy to detect by sight. It consists of a sandwich of some green material, often a copper compound, between two pieces of cut and polished quartz which form the top and bottom of the composite stone. Sometimes the backs of pale or off-colored emeralds and other beryls are painted with the color needed to strengthen them. There are even glass imitations for beryl that are quite successful, with the glass deliberately cracked and reheated to give the appearance of stones with natural flaws.

Pearl: Pearl is not strictly a mineral. It is derived from the excretions of a live animal and 10 to 14 percent of its mass is an organic substance called conchiolin. However, the greater part of the mass of a pearl consists of between 82 and 86 percent calcium carbonate—the mineral species aragonite—and it is included here because it has always held place among the more important and desirable gemstones.

Many kinds of shelled animal species can and do form pearls. However, most of these pearls are so grossly inferior in color, luster, and shape as to be useless for gem purposes. Only two species of mollusks seem able to produce pearls of value. In salt water the species Margaritifera, an oyster not related to our edible oyster, produces pearls in the best quantity and quality. The species Unio, a kind of mussel, is the freshwater source of good pearls.

Pearl formation is due to particles of sand, to tiny parasitic worms that bore through the shell, or to other irritating bits of material that stimulate the animal into trying to relieve itself of the annoyance. Sometimes the irritant is pushed against the inside of the shell and plastered over with layers of pearl to form flat or button-shaped "blister" pearls. At other times the irritant forces its way into the tissues of the animal. In this case it is apt to become covered equally on all sides with pearl to form a sphere. If for some reason the covering is not spherical, but is partially

FACING: *The great Hope, 44.5 carats—surprisingly, steel blue.*
ABOVE: *The Hope's story, still mysterious—Louis XIV's stolen French Blue reappeared in 1830 as the smaller Hope, in 1874 as a 6-carat piece in the Duke of Brunswick's collection.*

or extremely misshaped, the result is known as a baroque pearl.

The material that the mollusk produces to cover the irritant, as well as to line the entire inside of its shell, is called nacre. This consists of alternate layers of aragonite, deposited in many tiny overlapping plates, interbedded with layers of conchiolin. These tiny plates create the pearl's beautiful luster by causing light interference. They also help in identification, for because of them a real pearl will feel a little rough when it is scraped over the teeth.

The value of pearls depends on their shape, color, sheen, size, and origin. Color in pearls is an elusive quality that can usually be identified only by experts. Pure white or white with a faint tinge of pink or yellow are considered the most desirable colors. From time to time, usable pearls are found in fancy colors: yellow, bronze, pink, green, blue, black. These strongly colored pearls, however, rarely have a good luster, or "orient." Without this bright, lustrous sheen, a pearl drops considerably in value.

When the Japanese perfected a process that stimulated the oyster to place a thick layer of nacre over an artificially introduced irritant, the cultured-pearl industry was born. Experimentation established that the best starting material is a bead of mother-of-pearl—the nacreous material with which the mollusk lines its shell—cut from the shell of the pearl mussel of the Mississippi Valley. These beads, cut in various sizes, are inserted skillfully into the live oyster, and it is returned to the sea to continue growing. Treated oysters are kept in large growing rafts. From each of these rafts are suspended about sixty cages holding a total of three thousand oysters at a depth of seven to ten feet. They are inspected several times a year; after three to seven years the beads will have been coated with a layer of nacre almost one-sixteenth inch thick, and they are brought up and harvested.

Cultivated or natural, the pearl ranks as a major gemstone. If diamond is called the king of gems, pearl is queen.

Jade: The name jade refers not to one mineral species but to two—jadeite and nephrite—which have practically no relationship to each other except for a similarity of appearance. Jadeite is a sodium aluminum silicate occurring in white, emerald green, and other colors, and is one of a group of rock-forming minerals called pyroxenes. Nephrite is a calcium magnesium iron silicate occurring in colors ranging from white to spinach-green to black, and is one of a different group of rock-forming minerals called amphiboles. Both jadeite and nephrite are only about 6.5 in hardness, but are so tough that they will stand amazing amounts of abuse.

The ancient Chinese worked *yu* as early as 1000 B.C. Most of this jade apparently came from Khotan and Yarkand in Turkestan. Marco Polo, in his voyages, visited the area and described the mining methods. Under the sharp eye of a supervisor on shore the searcher would wade out into the stream, feeling for the jade boulders with his feet. When he touched what felt like one, he would work it to shore. This material

was all nephrite. It was not until about the eighteenth century that the fine-quality jadeite found in Burma reached China, beginning a classic period in which beautiful objects were carved from superb, imperial green jade. This kind of jade is still so highly prized that a one-inch piece may be worth as much as five thousand dollars. The art of jade carving was subsidized by Chinese royalty during the Ching Dynasty (1644-1912), so that it reached its peak in relatively modern times.

Opal: In the gem market the supply of hard-to-find precious opal fluctuates too much for it to establish a steady price structure. When good-quality opal is available, its life is unpredictable, for the gem, being quite brittle, may crack if

FACING: *Mediterranean coral diving—no longer profitable.*
ABOVE: *An exploratory adit—a horizontal tunnel—into the ruby-bearing gravels of Burma, at a time when the British were trying to revive flagging industry there.*

subjected to heat or a sharp blow. Further, it is not very hard, and surface scratches from constant wear can dull its sheen. Nevertheless, the beauty of opal is so exquisite that in recent years it has become a popular gemstone.

Opal is a compound of the elements silicon and oxygen, somewhat like quartz but different in its structure. The gem trade recognizes four kinds of precious opal: white, black, fire, and water. White opal has a pale or white body color as a background for its fire. Black opal may be

dark blue, dark green, dark gray, or black in body color. Fire opal and water opal are either transparent or translucent. Fire opal has a yellowish, orange, or orange-red color and may or may not exhibit fire, whereas water opal is colorless but has fire. Not all opal has beautiful color and fire; if it does not, it is called common opal.

All gem opal comes from a sedimentary environment, but there are surprisingly few good sources. Gem opal has been known for centuries, as indicated by its name, which comes from the

Examples of pegmatite minerals. ABOVE: *Gem morganite from San Diego County, California.* FACING: *Two gems from Minas Gerais, Brazil, step cut for best display of their color.* ABOVE: *3273-carat topaz.* BELOW: *2054-carat beryl.*

Sanskrit word *upala,* which means precious stone.

In 1889, white opal was found at White Cliffs, Australia; this was soon followed by other Australian discoveries. But opal did not have much of a commercial market until later in the nineteenth century, when black opal was found at Lightning Ridge, Australia. Recently, there has been a growing interest in the fire opal from Mexico. The Mexican deposits have been worked since 1835 and have produced superb gems, some of them over 50 carats.

To help protect opal from damage, it is mounted most frequently in pins and brooches, rather than in rings or bracelets, and is usually given some kind of metal backing.

The expensive, highly desirable gemstones that have been discussed are familiar—at least in name—to almost everyone. But there are many other gems that, for a variety of reasons, have remained less well known. Some of these follow, listed here alphabetically, rather than in the order of their popularity, value, or beauty.

Amber: This material is actually sap that flowed, in times past, from various species of trees, and became fossilized. The world-famed Baltic variety, for example, came from a species of pine tree. Amber is therefore of organic origin and not really a mineral, but like the pearl holds a valid place in any discussion of gem materials. The color varies through shades of yellow, brown, and red. Amber is well simulated by so many modern gums and artificial resins that it is extremely difficult to identify with certainty. Some artificial amber is even manufactured with insects embedded, as often occurs in natural amber. In determining the genuineness of such a specimen, the skeptic's only hope would be to identify the insect to see if it is truly an ancient species.

Benitoite: Discovered in 1907, benitoite has been included in the company of gemstones only in modern times. It is a chemically complex barium titanium silicate found only in San Benito

County, California, which gives it its name. A hardness of 6.5, strong fire, high brilliance, and a lovely sapphire-blue color make it an excellent gemstone. Unfortunately, it is so rare that it is available only as an expensive collector's item. The largest existing cut stone, now in the Smithsonian Institution, weighs 7.6 carats.

Chrysoberyl: Ordinary chrysoberyl has a hardness of 8.5, and occurs in a color range from yellow through grass-green to brown. It is a beryllium aluminum oxide occurring in good-quality natural crystals, often in attractive cyclic twin crystals.

In 1830 a variety of chrysoberyl was found in an emerald mine near Takovaja, in the Ural Mountains of Russia, that was green in daylight and red in artificial light. Since Czar Alexander II had just come of age, the gem material was named alexandrite in his honor. Later, in the gem gravels of Ceylon, larger and finer alexan-

drites were found. The largest of these cut stones recorded, 66 carats, is now in the Smithsonian Institution.

Alexandrite is so popular that it is as expensive as the traditionally most precious gems—diamond, ruby, sapphire, and emerald. Partially successful attempts have been made to imitate it with a color-changing variety of synthetic sapphire.

Another important variety of chrysoberyl has an extremely strong and sharp chatoyancy, which produces exquisite cat's-eyes when the stones are cut in round-topped cabochon form. The colors of these vary from a light honey-yellow-green to brown to almost black, but each color shows the strong bright line necessary for a good cat's-eye.

Coral: Like amber and pearl, coral is not actually a mineral, since it has been deposited in the sea by coral animals. However, it has always been considered a gem material for beads, jewelry, and carvings, and does consist of the mineral

Chinese jade cutters work with special art. LEFT: *Jade is sliced with a lapidary saw.* ABOVE: *Grinding wheel is used to carve out delicate features.* FACING: *The goddess K'wan-yin, an eleven-inch figurine of Burma jadeite.*

calcite. Most coral is white, but there are color variations from pale pink to a deep oxblood red. Coral fisheries are limited to very definite areas, because coral animals require a water temperature between 55 and 60 degrees Fahrenheit. Regular coral fishing goes on in Japanese, Malay, and Mediterranean waters, with the finest red coral coming from Algeria and Tunisia.

Euclase: Although it has a hardness of 7.5, this beryllium silicate has a very strong tendency to cleave, which detracts considerably from its value as a gemstone. It is difficult to cut and cannot tolerate hard wear. Nevertheless, it is rare and beautiful enough to remain in demand, especially among gem collectors. The color ranges from colorless to pale aquamarine to greenish-blue. Most of the gem-quality material is found near

Ouro Prêto, north of Rio de Janeiro, Brazil.

Feldspar: The feldspars are actually a family of several closely related minerals, most of which are usable as gem material in one form or another. The most important gemstones among them are varieties of the feldspar species orthoclase. The best known of these is moonstone, which has a beautiful schiller (see page 126) aptly described by the name of the gem. Since the schiller is caused by the interference of light, it is best revealed if the cabochon is cut parallel to the feldspar layers that cause the interference.

Another orthoclase variety is a clear, pale yellow to golden-yellow stone that comes only from the pegmatites at Itrongay, Madagascar. The color in this variety, used as gems, is caused by a small amount of iron in solid solution.

Garnet: As is the case with feldspars, garnets also comprise a family of mineral species with at least six important members. They are pyrope, almandine, spessartine, uvarovite, grossular, and andradite. All of these except uvarovite, the chromium-bearing garnet, furnish fine gemstones of various colors. All are hard enough—about 7—and all have a refractive index high enough to make them brilliant. If they have a major drawback it is that their color is sometimes so dense that they look opaque. Ruby-red pyrope, used in antique Bohemian garnet jewelry, is perhaps most popular, but the rich orange-red spessartine found in Virginia and elsewhere is more striking because of its unusual color. A bright emerald-green andradite found in Russia and Italy is called demantoid and, when the quality is good, sells at prices rivaling diamond, sapphire, and emerald.

Peridot: Peridot—a gem name for the common mineral species olivine—is easily simulated in glass and has little brilliance or fire. Its lack of luster and peculiar rich bottle-green to brown color give it a certain subtle charm, but a strong tendency to cleave and a hardness of only 6.5 have prevented it from achieving great popularity. Nevertheless, it persists as an offbeat sort of gemstone, not too expensive and generally available. Crystals suitable for gem-cutting come from Egypt, Burma, and Arizona.

Quartz: Quartz, although a single mineral species, has several gem varieties whose names derive from differences in color. It is common enough so that prices of the finished gems are within reach of nearly everyone. A hardness of 7 is sufficient for durability. Quartz, which is silicon dioxide, is the commonest mineral species in the crust of the earth. Many of its gem varieties, such as agate, onyx, tigereye, jasper, blood-

stone, prase, are opaque varieties used for cabochons, carvings, and art objects. The most popular faceted varieties are amethyst, citrine, and rock crystal. Citrine varies in color from a smoky brown to a golden yellow and often imitates the color of topaz, so that it is sold as Brazilian topaz. Much of the faceted quartz now on the market comes from Brazil.

Sphene: This calcium titanium silicate is one of the rarer minerals that produces good gemstones. It has a barely suitable hardness of 5.5, is brittle, and has some tendency to cleave. The beauty of the gems, however, makes these drawbacks seem irrelevant. They are yellowish, brownish, or greenish, very brilliant and transparent, and because of high dispersion have a fire greater than that of diamond. The best faceting-quality sphene comes from Switzerland, the Austrian Tyrol, and Baja California.

Topaz: There is a popular belief that "all topaz is yellow and all yellow stones are topaz." Neither of these notions is true. Topaz, an aluminum silicate containing fluorine, occurs in fine gem crystals of several colors. The commonest is colorless, but light blue shades resembling aquamarine are also readily available. In addition there are light green, light rose, and deep red varieties. Certain yellow Brazilian topaz turns bright pink when heated, and stones of this color are prepared by natives on a somewhat hit-or-miss basis. They never know in advance whether the material they are heating will react with the desired color change. The most highly prized stones are the color of rich sherry or muscatel wine. Because it occurs in sufficient quantities, prices for topaz gemstones have remained moderate.

Topaz has a good luster and its gems are brilliant and hard—8 on the scale—but it has a

Three exceptional gems, diversely treated. FACING, TOP: *A great blue heron of sodalite, cut in Germany.* FACING, LEFT: *330-carat Burmese Star of Asia, the second-largest blue star sapphire known.* FACING, RIGHT: *880-carat faceted kunzite from Brazil.*

discouraging tendency to cleave easily, so that care must be taken in handling it.

Tourmaline: Part of the popularity of tourmaline is based on its very wide color range. It is found in crystals of pink, magenta, green, blue, yellow, brown, black, and many subtle intermediate shades. Pink and emerald green are particularly popular. It is even possible to find crystals exhibiting two or more colors. Tourmaline is a complex borosilicate with a hardness of just over 7 and little tendency to cleave; it is durable and useful as a gem in most kinds of mountings. Even though its refractive index is too low for brilliance and its dispersion is too low to produce fire, its beautiful colors make it very desirable. As with topaz, quartz, and certain other gems, it occurs in sufficient quantity to keep prices moderate.

Zircon: The high refractive index of zircon, a zirconium silicate, gives it brilliance, and its high dispersion gives it fire enough to substitute for diamond. Its colors range from blue and golden brown to no color at all. Zircon has a hardness of over 7, and it is readily found in parts of Thailand, Viet Nam, Laos, and also in the rich gem-laden gravels of Burma and Ceylon.

THE LAPIDARY ARTS: Before a gem material becomes a gem, it must pass through the hands of the lapidary—the man who uses many techniques to cut each specimen so that it achieves its most beautiful, or most salable, potential.

Very little was done to take the fullest, most carefully calculated advantage of gem rough until the seventeenth century. Before that time the general procedure was to grind and polish existing crystal faces to increase their transparency and reflecting ability. It was also customary among ancient lapidaries to round off the tops of some of the more colorful, opaque gem fragments. We still do something of this sort today when we tumble pieces of gem material with abrasives until they assume a high polish but retain their free form.

The opaque gem materials, such as turquoise and jade, are still characteristically cut by being rounded off to produce a relatively large, dome-shaped surface with few conflicting reflections, so that the color or pattern is well displayed. Such stones are called cabochons—a word derived from the Old French, *cabo*, meaning head—referring to their rounded tops. There are simple cabochons with dome-shaped tops and flat bottoms, double cabochons with domes at top and bottom, and hollow cabochons with domed top and scooped-out or concave bottoms. Very deep-colored garnets are traditionally cut as hollow cabochons to reduce their thickness and thus allow enough light through to show the color. There is also the tallow-topped cabochon, with a dome so low that it is shaped like a drop of wax that has fallen on a cold surface.

Aside from use with opaque materials, the cabochon is also used for cutting cat's-eye and star

a

b

c

d

e

f

g

h

i

j

k

*Opal characteristics reveal
their sources. Mexican stones (b, c, f, g, i, j)
have gelatinous clarity, small color flashes.
Australian opals (a, d, e, h)
are opaque white, black or gray,
with larger flecks of fire.
Brazilians (k) resemble the Australian.*
FACING: *A magnificent jeweled
crown enriches this detail from
Van Eyck's "Virgin and Donor."*

99

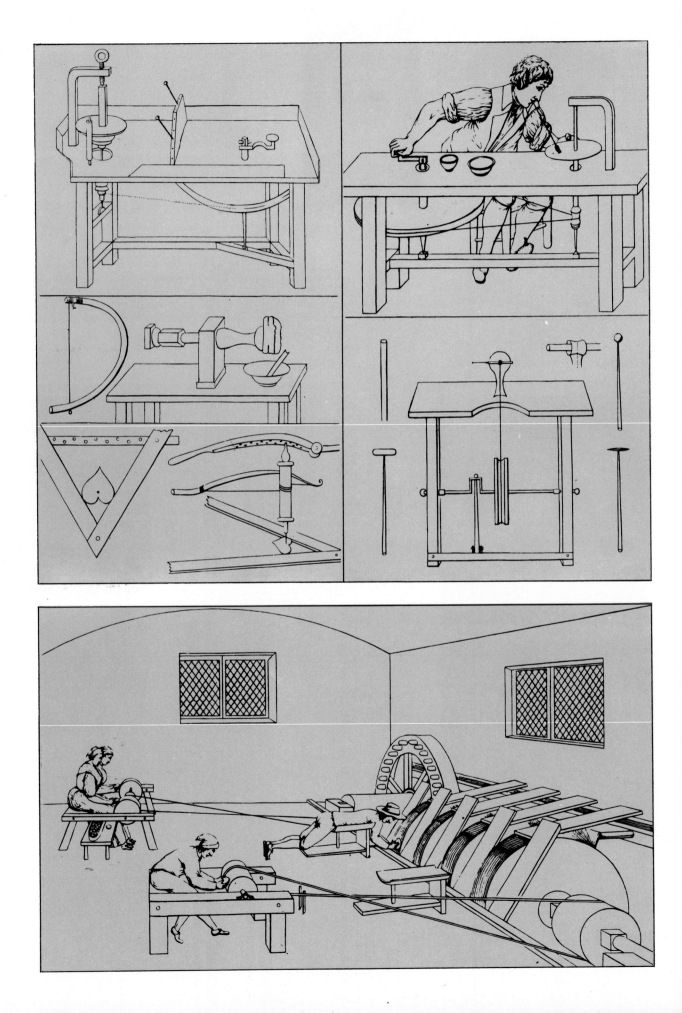

stones. A bead is a circular double cabochon with both domes equally developed. Very large beads, or spheres, are often mounted or displayed as art objects. The most extraordinary sphere in existence is a flawless one at the Smithsonian Institution cut from a thousand-pound fragment of Burmese quartz. It weighs one hundred six and three-quarter pounds.

The finest and most expensive gem materials are always cut as faceted stones. These are transparent gems with a series of carefully placed flat, reflecting faces. In general, to describe a faceting cut, the stone is divided into sections. The flat top is called the table, and the facets appearing above the middle of the stone are in the part called the crown. The middle is called the girdle. Below the girdle the facets lie in the pavilion. If there is a tiny flat face at the bottom of the gem, opposite from the table, it is called a culet.

The exact angles for placement of these facets are different for every kind of gem material. For different purposes there have also been developed a number of standard patterns of faces. The most frequently used symmetrical cuts are the standard brilliant cut and the step cut. Modern jewelry design often calls for the baguette, cut-corner triangle, kite, epaulette, keystone, marquise, and many more. Frequently the kind of setting to be used determines the size and cut of the gem.

Cutting requires three basic operations: sawing, grinding, and polishing. Sawing is usually done with a rapidly turning disk of iron or bronze edged with diamond. The stone is carefully pressed against this edge and the diamond saw scratches its way through. Oil or water is used to bathe the saw and keep it from getting too hot. The second operation is grinding. Again, this makes use of a rapidly rotating horizontal disk—or

"lap"—charged on its surface with a water paste of an abrasive like corundum or powdered diamond. The last operation, using the same kind of disk, is polishing. This time the lap is charged with an extremely fine abrasive such as jewelers' rouge, or tin oxide, or finely powdered pumice.

Polishing is not merely the removal of surface scratches. The surface being polished often reaches the melting point, causing the mineral to flow and deposit a very thin glaze over its own surface, which obliterates scratches and other imperfections.

Perhaps the greatest form of artistic expression in working gem materials is carving. Everyone familiar with the jade carving of the Ching Dynasty in China appreciates not only the skill and patience of the carvers, but also the extraordinary characteristics of jade—toughness and tenacity—which permit this kind of carving.

Other cultures, at other times, have specialized in the carving techniques known as intaglio and cameo. Intaglio carving is incised into the gem

FACING, TOP: *Grinding and engraving tools, from an eighteenth-century lapidary shop.* LEFT: *At Idar-Oberstein, Germany, a lapidary center since Roman times, the Old Mill is still in use.* ABOVE: *The ancient crown of Charlemagne—part of the Imperial Treasure displayed in Vienna's Palace Museum.*

101

and is usually intended for seals. Cameo carving is raised above the surface rather than incised. Both of these are often done in gem materials that contain layers of various colors, so that the raised or incised carvings are of different color from the background. Agate and shell are used most often.

Anyone who cuts, polishes, carves, or otherwise forms gem materials into objects of beauty considers himself—and is properly named—a lapidary. Because of the importance of diamond, however, anyone who cuts diamonds considers himself, and is known in the trade, as a diamond-cutter.

GEM IMITATIONS AND SUBSTITUTES: The number of natural stones appears really insignificant when compared with the number of gem imitations and substitutes that are being marketed. Imitation, assembled, reconstructed, and synthetic gems appear in great quantities, and usually without any attempt at deception or fraud. Unfortunately, even when not used intentionally for fraud, they have created confusion and apprehension in the minds of the gem-buying public.

Synthetics: All of the major gem minerals have been duplicated in the laboratory. To be commercially useful, laboratory methods must produce material of sufficient quality and size to be cut, and also to compete in price with gems dug from the earth. Good diamond, for example, is now manufactured in quantity, but cannot be made in pieces sufficiently large to be cut into gems.

The production of synthetic ruby and sapphire for gems has been infinitely more successful. Cleverly synthesized rubies appeared in the early 1880s. These "Geneva rubies" were reconstructed by heating together small fragments of natural ruby until they fused into a single mass that could be cut. But Verneuil's chalumeau made the method obsolete. Sapphires are also easily made by Verneuil's method, substituting titanium and iron for the chromium oxide that is used in the ruby-making process. In the Verneuil method powdered aluminum oxide, containing the chromium, iron, or titanium coloring agents, is sieved down through the flame of a vertical blowtorch furnace. As it passes through the flame, it forms a single crystal boule, or tapered cylinder of the synthetic gem material. In a few hours a boule of several hundred carats can be formed.

In recent years a method has even been found to make star rubies and star sapphires. The boules are prepared by adding between .1 and .3 percent of titanium oxide to the feed materials in the Verneuil furnace. After forming, the boules are heated to just over 2000 degrees Fahrenheit, at which time the added titanium oxide forms thou-

sands of tiny needle crystals that line themselves up in the direction of the sapphire or ruby structure. Actually, the stars look so much better than most natural star stones that they are very easily detected.

Spinel is another gemstone successfully synthesized. Natural spinel, except for its red variety, has never been popular. Because of this, most synthetic spinel is manufactured to simulate gemstones of other species. It can very easily masquerade as fine-colored aquamarine, blue zircon, green tourmaline, pale green emerald, and can approximate a greenish-yellow variety of chrysoberyl. There is even a synthetic spinel that has the proper white, milky appearance of moonstone. All of this spinel is made by the Verneuil method, substituting magnesium oxide for part of the aluminum oxide.

There are two other gemstones made by the Verneuil method that are good enough to market but that do not appear in nature as gem material. In 1948, synthetic rutile was offered for sale under the name Titania. This is an appropriate name because, like natural rutile, the material is titanium oxide. The feed material is pure titanium oxide. It is passed through a Verneuil furnace that has been modified by the addition of an extra jet of oxygen. These boules come out black and are later heated in a stream of oxygen, at which time they change from black to deep blue to light blue to green to pale yellow. Heating can be stopped at any point to retain a particular color. The gemstones cut from these boules have a hardness of 6 to 6.5, show very strong double refraction, and dispersion six times that of diamond. The flashes of fire caused by this extreme dispersion are far beyond anything diamond can approach.

The second material is strontium titanate, which is not found in nature at all, but has been sold

FACING: *The finest known tourmaline from San Diego County, California—an extraordinary fourteen-inch specimen still in matrix.* ABOVE: *Sardonyx cabochons from Serrado Mar, Brazil—often simulated by dyed agate.*

since 1955 under the name Fabulite, as well as under other names, which suggest that it looks like diamond. This synthetic gemstone is bright and colorless and has a dispersion four times that of diamond.

Some other gems, like quartz, are made by a hydrothermal method. Quartz itself can be a gemstone, but synthetic quartz does not compete in price with natural quartz for this purpose. Synthetic emerald competes easily with natural emerald. There have been various successful attempts to make emerald, but the first stones to be successfully marketed were prepared by Carroll F. Chatham of San Francisco, California. He has been producing excellent emeralds of good color, by a process he says is hydrothermal, using crushed beryl as feed material and perhaps a small natural crystal as a seed. Details of Mr. Chatham's method have never been divulged.

There is a newer process developed in the Austrian Tyrol that has fascinating possibilities. The process is again hydrothermal, using crushed beryl as feed material. In this case, however, the seed is a faceted stone of pale green beryl over which an emerald coating is grown. When completed, the overgrown facets need only be repolished and the stone is ready for sale.

Imitations: The commonest imitator of gemstones is glass, despite the fact that it is not always satisfactory. One variety of glass that is produced by melting natural beryl has none of the characteristics of crystalline beryl, but can be cut into surprisingly good gems. Normally, however, a common lead glass is used with various coloring materials, such as chromic oxide for green, cobalt oxide for blue, and didymium oxide for pink. The brilliance of a cut stone is sometimes enhanced by coating the back with a mercury amalgam, such as is used on mirrors, or by putting a layer of metal foil behind it in a closed jewelry mounting. Various kinds of plastics are also used with a similar effect.

Composites: For centuries it has been common practice to build up gemstones by fusing or cementing a shaped piece of natural gemstone to another piece, or pieces, of inferior or artificial material. If this is done with care, and the joints are artfully concealed in jewelry mountings, the composite stones can be very deceptive. The commonest kind is a doublet in which the top is a thin piece of garnet and the bottom is a colored glass. The garnet, fastened to the glass by heating, furnishes a hard protective cover. Because this cover is so thin, its color is weak, so that the whole stone takes on the hue of the glass underneath.

Other doublets have been made in which both top and bottom are genuine, but are separate pieces glued together so that a larger gem can be made from two smaller or badly shaped pieces. Still others have the top made of the authentic gemstone other than garnet but the bottom of glass. A glass cabochon with a backing of iridescent abalone shell looks like a passable opal. Thin slabs of precious Australian opal are often fastened to a backing of the matrix rock from which the opal comes. Even triplets are sometimes made, in which the colored material is sandwiched between a top and bottom layer of natural sapphire or natural quartz.

Artificial coloring: There are several methods used to intensify or change the coloring or apparent coloring of a gemstone One direct method used for diamonds is to treat them in an atomic reactor, which converts off-colors into more beautiful hues of tan, yellow, and green.

The color of the best golden-brown, sky blue, and colorless zircon offered by jewelers has been induced in the stones by heating reddish-brown zircon pebbles under controlled conditions to temperatures near 1800 degrees Fahrenheit.

There are also indirect methods that add something to the stone that was not there originally. A colored foil backing behind a stone of poor color, in a closed mounting, cannot be seen and will change the gem's color. It is even possible to paint or dye the back facets. A violet dye on pavilion facets of a yellow diamond will make it look almost colorless. It is not unusual to find colorless Mexican opal painted black on the back of the cabochon or fastened to a piece of black glass, which gives it a dark background to show off its internal fire.

Turquoise impregnated with wax or plastic to deepen its color, pale gray jade that is dyed green to look like imperial jade, and agate dyed red or blue or black or almost any color—these are only a few of the examples of the ingenious practice of color alteration in gems.

Faceted or carved, colorless or of brilliant hues, soft or hard, in jewelry or out, expensive or not, gems are universally admired.

FACING: *Dazzling light patterns refracted and reflected by a 2680-carat Brazilian topaz, the size of half a grapefruit.* ABOVE: *An unset triplet clearly reveals its composition. Well set, it will appear to be a solid gem.*

Wonders of the Kingdom

4

*The known mineral world is full
of spectacular phenomena—the unknown
may hold unimaginable wonders*

Rocks that float, rocks that burn, rocks that glow with bright colors in the dark, rocks that look like plants and animals—these are some of the wonders of the mineral kingdom. But what makes minerals particularly fascinating to scientists and amateurs alike is that many of them demonstrate the operation of physical laws in spectacular ways.

MINERALS AND LIGHT: The interaction between certain minerals and light produces a number of effects that are not only astonishing but extremely useful. One of the more familiar is *fluorescence.*

Ads that urge the American housewife to use one detergent or another so that her white clothes will be "whiter and brighter" are not merely huckstering devices. Some detergents contain small amounts of a colorless dye, invisibly applied to the wash during the washing process, which reacts to the sun's rays by glowing with a white light. Your wash, consequently, looks whiter and brighter. This phenomenon is known as photoluminescence, and is familiar to anyone who has seen traffic markers, sweaters, or bathing suits that have been dyed with photoluminescent substances to make them visible at a great distance.

The study of photoluminescence began shortly after Sir Isaac Newton (1642-1727) made his important discoveries about light. Newton, in addition to the many other achievements of his extraordinary career, discovered that a triangular glass prism could split a beam of sunlight into a rainbow or spectrum of colors. This proved beyond a doubt that white light is merely a mixture of several colors or wavelengths of light, emerging from the prism in a strict order from red (the longest) through orange, yellow, green, blue, and indigo to violet (the shortest). Since Newton's time, it has been discovered that this rainbow or spectrum is very much broader than was originally thought, but that only the section from red to violet is visible to the human eye. The shorter wavelengths just beyond violet are called ultraviolet and the longer wavelengths just beyond red are called infrared. Ultraviolet light must be handled carefully; the shortest wavelengths can injure the eyes.

The discovery of the color spectrum stimulated new research. In 1852, Sir George G. Stokes, a British physicist, discovered that the mineral fluorite, when exposed to short wavelengths, would absorb them, convert them to longer wavelengths, and give them off again. He called this behavior fluorescence, a term still widely used in place of photoluminescence. To the mineral-specimen collector, this short-to-long wavelength conversion, known as Stokes' Law, is familiar as a superb display of bright, attractive colors given off by fluorescent mineral specimens under ultraviolet light.

Whether or not a mineral is fluorescent depends on the presence of certain activators. These are traces of particular elements which may be part of the composition of the mineral or may be present as impurities—in which case, as with calcite, the mineral is fluorescent only when the proper impurity is present. Common activators are manganese, copper, silver, lead, uranium, and chromium. The red color of ruby (Al_2O_3) derives from a small amount of chromium impurity, which

PRECEDING PAGES: *English fluorite centers a fluorescent display. From lower
left: autunite, North Carolina; calcite, willemite, Franklin, New Jersey; hyalite,
North Carolina; wernerite, Ontario; calcite and willemite samples, Franklin.*

of the electrons absorb it, thereby becoming overenergetic and moving out of normal position. They immediately attempt to get rid of this extra energy and return to their original positions. The trapped surplus energy is given off as a tiny bit of light and all returns to normal. When this is done simultaneously by millions of atoms of the mineral, all the bits of ejected light added together produce the fluorescent glow.

Any human being who has ever tried to walk through a closed glass door or gazed through diving goggles at a spiny lobster in tropical waters must marvel at the phenomenon we call *transparency*. We are told that light travels through glass, water, and other substances, emerging intact on the other side. We are puzzled, however, as to how the light, bearing its images, can actually get through these objects. And if it can go through some solids and liquids, why not through others?

The fact is light doesn't "go through" anything. What happens is that light hits the atoms in these solids or liquids and, by its energy, starts them vibrating sympathetically. These vibrations are passed through the structure from atom to atom. If the atoms are properly aligned, the vibrations will move as in a row of falling dominoes. They are then ejected at the other side in the identical form in which they entered. The light does not trickle slowly through spaces between the atoms, as though finding its way through a maze. On the contrary, since the responsive vibrations are extremely rapid, the light travels at a rate approximating the 670 million miles per hour at which unimpeded light travels from one place to another.

Color in minerals results from a complex series of interactions. Once we accept the fact that the passage of light through a mineral substance is subject to the way the mineral's atoms are ar-

is also the activator for its reddish fluorescence. The bright pink fluorescence of calcite and the bright green of willemite from the Franklin, New Jersey, mines are both due to traces of manganese which excite different fluorescent colors in the two different mineral species. Too much of the manganese activator, strangely enough, prevents fluorescence.

The cause of fluorescence lies within the atoms of which the minerals are composed. Each atom is made up of many extraordinary particles. Among these are electrons, which account in large part for the appearance and behavior of the atom. Each electron has a relatively fixed position and a fixed amount of energy within the atom. When the mineral is exposed to ultraviolet light some

Sir Isaac Newton (1642-1727) founded mechanics, the science of optics, and discovered, among other physical facts, the color spectrum. Legend—almost certainly untrue—holds that his theory of gravity was inspired by a falling apple.

ranged, it is easy to see that there might be alterations along the way. This tampering does not usually involve a change in wavelength; it is rather that the atoms may be selective about what wavelengths or colors they will permit to pass. If they are arranged so that only red passes, then red is all that emerges. Consequently, the mineral appears transparent, or partially transparent, red. If only green passes, the mineral will be transparent green. All the rest of the vibrations are absorbed in the labyrinthine arrangements of atoms. This, then, is a major source of color in transparent minerals or, for that matter, in all transparent objects. If the mineral stops the passage of all light it looks opaque and black. Black is the absence of all visible wavelengths.

The color of a mineral, even if it is opaque, seen by light reflecting from its surface, results from a similar but opposite cause. Often, as a substance is struck by white light, some wavelengths are transmitted through it, some are absorbed, and some are not permitted to enter but are bounced back, or reflected. If the reflected wavelength is blue, the object looks blue. On the other hand the object can be red as we look at

the light through it, since red could be the wavelength transmitted. Thus an object can appear to be different colors at the same time, depending on whether we see it by reflected light or by transmitted light.

Minerals are sometimes found to be different colors in different deposits. Fluorite, for example, is found at various mines in specimens of blue, green, pink, yellow, brown, purple, and black. Absolutely pure fluorite is colorless. Any color in it, apparently, must come from something added to it that is not typical of pure fluorite. Colored minerals of this type are called allochromatic: the color is due to traces of impurities or to defects in the arrangement of atoms in the structure. There are other minerals that have a characteristic color not dependent on impurities. Sulfur, for

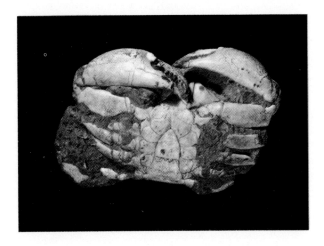

example, is always bright yellow when pure. These are called idiochromatic minerals.

In addition to sifting and sorting the wavelengths of light, minerals are capable of *bending* it. This is fortunate, for otherwise we would have no lenses for telescopes, microscopes, or eyeglasses, all of which depend on the bending of light to operate. Lenses are designed to bend rays of light, making them converge upon the eye in such a way as to produce the illusion of magnification. To prove this put a pencil on a slant halfway into a glass of water. The pencil looks bent where it enters the water. Light traveling from certain substances to others—such as air to water or water to glass or air to glass—bends. The amount of light-bending that takes place depends largely on what materials are involved. Bending is extreme if there is a great difference in the density of the materials between which the light is passing. For example, there is more bending when light passes from air into glass than when it passes from water into glass.

Many crystalline mineral species bend or refract light in two directions at the same time. In such a case, a light beam is actually split into two parts, each being bent to a different degree. This is called double refraction.

Refraction and double refraction result from the way atoms in a mineral affect light pouring through it. As the degree of refraction differs for each mineral, it can be used as an aid in identification.

To say that all the reaction between light and minerals is due to the kinds of atoms present and their arrangement would be an oversimplification. There are certain other color effects that are caused by structural defects, or by the presence of relatively large impurities. One of the more interesting of these processes is called *interference*.

Interference colors are usually explained by invoking images of thin films, such as an oil slick on a rain-wet street, which often produce a lovely liquid rainbow. A ray of light strikes a thin layer of oil at a particular angle. Some of the ray is reflected immediately. Some of it penetrates the film and, in turn, is reflected from the contact surface between the oil and water. This second portion, traveling back through the oil film, continues on its way parallel to the first ray fraction. This means that the light waves in the two parts bouncing back are out of step with each other. The resulting combination is seen by the observer as a different mixture of wavelengths from the original ray or, by definition and appearance, a different blend of color. The hue produced as these wavelengths interfere with each other depends upon the thickness of the oil film and the angle at which light strikes it.

The beautiful blue glow, or schiller (German for play of colors), exhibited by peristerite is caused by light interference of this kind. In this case the thin films are actually the layers of thin plates of which this feldspar mineral is formed.

Feldspar exhibits another light effect called *aventurescence*. In some samples of feldspar there

Preserved for eons in sedimentary rock, fossils must be exposed by careful handwork. FACING, FAR LEFT: *Eurypterid from the Midwest.* LEFT: *Crinoids, same area.* ABOVE: *"Swimming crab" from Panama.*

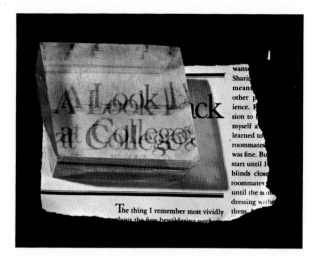

are innumerable microscopic plates of the minerals hematite or goethite. These plates, often red-orange, are scattered throughout the almost colorless feldspar but are arranged parallel to each other. As light penetrates the feldspar, it is reflected at the same instant from myriads of these tiny, flat inclusions. Such feldspar is fittingly named sunstone or aventurine. Other mineral species, of course, can be aventurescent. One variety of quartz, for example, which contains tiny reflecting plates, usually mica, is also called aventurine.

Since the effects of interference and aventurescence are both found in certain kinds of feldspar, the two phenomena may occur in the same specimen. This phenomenon is called *labradorescence*, from its appearance in a calcium-rich feldspar called labradorite. It appears as large patches of iridescent blue and green color with occasional reds and yellows. Most of this effect is due to the same light interference as is found in peristerite. Some of the color flashes, however, are caused by the reflection of light from numberless platelets of black magnetite which are arranged as parallel inclusions.

RADIOACTIVE MINERALS: Legend has it that Henri Becquerel, professor of physics at the Museum of Natural History in Paris, accidentally discovered radioactivity in 1896 by inadvertently leaving some uranium ores on wrapped photographic plates in a drawer. This is a romantic story, but does Becquerel little justice. Actually, X-rays had been discovered and announced by Röntgen earlier that year. Becquerel undertook experiments of his own with a synthetic uranium compound—potassium uranyl sulfate—to see if he could produce X-rays by the action of the sun's rays on fluorescent materials. He thought he had done it because in one experiment his compound, placed in the sun on a covered photographic plate, fogged the plate as X-rays would have done. As sun was necessary to further experiment, during a spell of cloudy weather a batch of plates and the uranium compound were left together in a drawer. It was five days before the weather cleared. Though suspecting that the plates would be ruined after so long a delay, Becquerel, a careful scientist, developed them anyway, and found to his surprise that the sun had not been necessary to cause the compound to fog the photographic plates quite badly. They had mysteriously become fogged while locked in the dark drawer!

Subsequently, he found that nothing he could do would stop, start, or otherwise affect this strange radiation. The only requirement seemed to be that the element uranium or thorium had to be present in the substances he used to produce the penetrating rays. But unlike X-rays, Becquerel's strange rays were no good for taking pictures. Consequently they created little interest, even among scientists.

At about the same time, Marja Sklodowska Curie (1867-1934), intrigued by Becquerel's discoveries about radioactivity, began work on the radioactive substances in pitchblende as a project

ABOVE: *A calcite cleavage shows the mineral's excellent double refraction.* FACING: *Two optical phenomena as illustrated in a nineteenth-century book on natural philosophy.* TOP: *Refraction.* RIGHT: *Reflection.*

for her doctor's degree. Eventually, Madame Curie and her husband (who had been her physics professor at the Sorbonne) found that these strange penetrating rays had sources other than uranium and thorium. In 1898, they discovered polonium, which they named for the then nonexistent Poland that was Madame Curie's homeland, and radium, named for the intensity of the radiations that this element gave off. Further experimentation demonstrated that these strange natural rays were far more penetrating than X-rays and far more deadly to living tissues.

Polonium and radium, interesting as they are, appear only as traces of impurities in other radioactive minerals. Usually when we speak of radioactive minerals we mean uranium minerals, because uranium is by far the commonest of radioactive elements. It is one of a group of elements that characteristically form highly colored compounds; uranium minerals are bright red, orange, yellow, and green. The only major exception is uraninite—uranium oxide (UO_2)—which is jet black.

The remarkable thing about radioactive minerals is not only what they do, but what happens to them after it is done. Uranium atoms that undergo the radioactive experience seem to disappear, to be mysteriously replaced by atoms of some other element, usually lead. For centuries, alchemists had worked unsuccessfully at the transmutation of elements, trying to convert common metals into gold. All this time nature had been busy transmuting uranium into lead, a truly remarkable feat.

For an atom of one element to become an atom of another, nature must tamper with the inner mechanism of the atom itself. A uranium atom has 92 particles called protons in its dense central core or nucleus, as well as 146 neutrons. At un-

predictable intervals some of the neutrons are violently disrupted, upsetting the balance of things. Parts of the nucleus are then ejected at enormous velocities. These atomic projectiles have been labeled alpha (α), beta (β), and gamma (γ) radiation by physicists, and the characteristics of the radiation have been carefully described. After the disturbance subsides, there are 82 protons left with 124 neutrons. This is an atom of lead. The results are always the same, but it is impossible to predict which atom will be transmuted next from uranium to lead.

For our purposes, one important fact is known. In five billion years, half of any given mass of uranium atoms will become lead. This time interval is called the half-life of uranium: in five billion years half of the uranium will be converted. The rate is as steady as the most accurate clock and cannot be changed.

This fact can be an invaluable guide for determining the age of rock deposits in the earth. For example: A specimen of rock is obtained that contains some uranium minerals. To determine exactly how old this specimen is, one must simply determine the amount of uranium and lead present, then calculate to see how long a time has been necessary to produce this quantity of lead in proportion to the remaining unconverted quantity of uranium. We then know the date when nature put the uranium in the rock or, in other words, the age of the rock itself. This method has dated some of the world's oldest known rocks, showing them consistent with the determination of astronomers that the earth was formed about two billion years ago.

All the remarkable mineral characteristics we have discussed, up to this point, have been demonstrations of energy being absorbed, changed, or ejected. However, the wondrous appearance of many mineral objects such as concretions, geodes, stalactites, meteorites, and pseudomorphs is actually the result of energies and conditions that created them in the first place.

CONCRETIONS: Roughly rounded masses of mineral, formed when some material is deposited around some kind of center or nucleus, are called concretions. They are found embedded within an enclosing rock, not just resting in holes or cavities in the rock. Since they are usually harder than the rock surrounding them, they often remain intact even when their rock covering is worn away by erosion.

Some concretions began as rather stiff, gummy lumps that rolled around picking up leaves, shells, twigs, and other debris. Eventually these lumps hardened and were buried or trapped in sedimentary rock beds. Other concretions were apparently formed by water seeping through sediments, dissolving some substances and later depositing this material in cavities in sedimentary rock. It is even possible for the concretion to grow in the sedimentary rock itself and not in a cavity, pushing the host material aside to make room.

Concretions occur in many shapes: spherical, ball-shaped, branchlike, flattened, oval, rootlike. They can look like strings of beads, toy-balloon animals, human portraits, modern sculptures, solidified plants—almost anything imaginable. They vary in size from small, like the claystone concretions left by the Ice Age in New Jersey and southern New England clays, to specimens up to thirty feet long, found in the sandstones of Texas.

Concretions are usually composed of the minerals calcite, quartz, hematite, limonite, siderite, pyrite, and marcasite, as well as clays. The beautiful green gem mineral variscite, an aluminum phos-

TOP: *Petrified wood from Clover Creek, Idaho.* RIGHT: *An insect trapped ages ago in flowing sap remains imprisoned in an amber fragment from the Baltic Sea area.*

phate found in Utah, occurs as concretions formed in limestone. The brassy, metallic mineral pyrite is often found as concretions in coal beds.

GEODES: Geodes are sphere-shaped stones, usually at least partially hollow, and often lined inside with sparkling mineral crystals or concentric layers of minerals.

Magnificent geodes make the area of Rio Grande do Sul in Brazil, and the adjoining part of Uruguay, notable sources of fine amethyst. In these regions, ancient volcanic rocks are filled with cavities which were produced by large steam bubbles at the time of formation. These bubble cavities later became lined with crystals of amethyst and agate deposited from solutions of seeping water.

From Rio Grande do Sul came the most fantastic geode known—thirty-three feet in length, sixteen and a half feet in width, and ten feet in height, with an estimated weight of seventy thousand pounds. Its interior was lined with tons of beautiful purple amethyst crystals, many of them several inches across, with glittering crystal faces. This geode provided many fine gemstones. Several sections were preserved intact, including a piece weighing four hundred pounds, which is now at the Smithsonian Institution.

Amethyst is a purple variety of the common mineral quartz, which is usually white or colorless. Quartz is the most common material found in the cavities of geodes. It appears in many colors, depending on what impurities have been gathered in during the lining operation and how rapidly this operation has taken place. Slow deposition, with relatively few impurities in the quartz, tends to leave the cavity lined with sparkling crystals of various colors and sizes. Rapid deposition will often fill the cavity with beautiful, varicolored bands or patterns of extremely fine-grained quartz called agate.

Geodes are especially common in the limestones of the Mississippi and Ohio River Valleys. Large quantities of interesting and attractive geodes are also being found in Chihuahua, Mexico. Their contents include quartz crystals of amethyst color, smoky color, gray, white, lavender, and brown, along with contrastingly colored crystals of calcite, goethite, and other minerals.

STALACTITES: Anyone who has seen a row of icicles forming on the edge of his roof has witnessed the birth of stalactites. With a change in temperature, these beautiful spears are gone forever. But fortunately nature also makes them elsewhere of durable minerals, so that they can be preserved and admired.

A common occurrence of stalactites is in the numerous limestone caverns scattered round the world. The Luray Caverns and the Endless Caverns in Virginia, the Carlsbad Caverns in New Mexico and many others are filled with rock icicles of all sizes and varied shapes. The varia-

tion in shape is caused by changes in the direction of water flow and in the rate of flow, producing curved and fluted, fat and short, long and thin, single or clustered groups of stalactites. On the floors of these caverns stalagmites rise up to meet their pendant cousins, as the drops spill down to deposit more material below.

Stalactites need not be white. In some Arizona mines, impurities of copper minerals tint the stalactites a beautiful shade of green or bluish-green. Iron impurities can make stalactites pale yellow, brown or reddish-brown. Soldiers stationed at the not-so-solid Rock of Gibraltar used to occupy their long hours by carving various objects from the stalactitic onyx, banded and patterned in tan, brown, and yellow, found in the limestone caves of that famous site. And although aragonite and calcite are the most common stalactite minerals, these unusual forms are sometimes composed of barite, marcasite, limonite, and malachite as well.

METEORITES: The passage of celestial objects through the earth's atmosphere is a phenomenon that has created widespread amazement since man

FACING, TOP: *Henri Becquerel, discoverer of radioactivity.*
LEFT: *A meteorite fall at L'Aigle, France, in 1803.*
ABOVE: *Pierre and Marie Curie.* RIGHT: *A pinch of radium at one foot for one hour took the Curies' first radiograph.*

first looked up at the heavens. The first observed meteorite fall from which actual samples are still preserved occurred at Ensisheim, near the French-German border. An eyewitness reported:

"On Wednesday, November 7, the night before St. Martins' Day in the year of our Lord 1492, a singular miracle happened: for between the hours of eleven and twelve a loud clap of thunder took place, with a long continued noise, which was heard at a great distance: and a stone fell from the heavens in the Ban of Ensisheim which weighed two hundred sixty pounds... it was a miracle of God: because, before that time, nothing of the kind has ever been heard of, seen or described.

"When this stone was found, it had entered the earth to a depth equal to the height of a man. What everybody asserted was, that it had been the will of God that it should be found.

"And when King Maximilian was here, the Monday after Saint Catherine's Day of the same year, his Excellency ... gave orders that it should be suspended in the church and that no person should be permitted to take any part of it. His Excellency however took two fragments: one of which he kept and the other he gave to Duke Sigismund of Austria."

Contrary to orders, specimen samples were removed, and can now be found in several major meteorite collections as well as in the Ensisheim Church.

Early public discussion about meteorites and shooting stars had all the characteristics of present-day speculation about flying saucers. Thomas Jefferson, on hearing a report by Professors Silliman and Kingsley of Yale University concerning the fall of a meteorite in Connecticut in 1807, is reported to have said that it was easier to believe that two Yankee professors would lie than that stones should fall from heaven.

But stones do fall from the heavens, and in large quantities. Estimates indicate that four hundred million individual meteors penetrate the earth's atmosphere every day, and that twenty million of these become bright enough to photograph. This means that space is filled with celestial debris swept up by the gravity of earth as it rushes on its way around the sun at 18.5 miles a second. The greatest part of this material is destroyed by the heat caused by the friction of its rocketlike passage through the air. But each

FACING: *Eroded remnants at Monument Park, Colorado, drawn from an early photograph.* TOP: *Four-foot concretions weathered out of shale near Tyrone, Pennsylvania.*
ABOVE: *Clay concretions from Vermont—often called mudstones.*

year some few pieces survive, fall on the earth, and are recovered. Four such recoveries in one year is considered remarkably good luck.

Meteorites are eagerly sought for scientific research, since they are our only samples of the universe that do not come from earth. Our current interest in space sciences has stimulated research on meteorites, and a good deal is now known of their composition and appearance. They are classified as iron meteorites, stony meteorites, stony-iron meteorites, and tektites.

Iron meteorites, or siderites, are made of an alloy containing about 91 percent iron and 8.5 percent nickel, with traces of some other minerals often present.

A typical *stony meteorite,* or aerolite, has a black, glassy crust because its surface has melted during its scorching passage through earth's atmosphere. When the crust is broken, a fine-grained stony interior is revealed. Stony meteorites are subdivided into two groups, chondrites and achondrites, depending upon their textures. The chondrites contain small chondri, which are round bodies composed of the minerals olivine or py-

ABOVE: *Cascading pools in the archaeologically famous limestone cave of Domica in Czechoslovakia.* FACING: *Pumice, light enough to float, is formed from molten igneous rock of volcanic origin which has been made frothy by gas bubbles.*

roxene. Achondrites do not have these bodies. Chondrites will have as much as 12 percent nickel-iron, but achondrites only about 1 percent. Other minerals present include enstatite, diopside, feldspar, and olivine.

Stony-iron meteorites, or siderolites, contain about equal amounts of metal and stone. The stony part is usually olivine with some pyroxene, and is found as large rounded grains scattered throughout the whole spongelike metal mass of this kind of meteorite.

Tektites are the subject of considerable theorizing. Not all scientists agree that they are, in fact, meteorites. In any event, tektites are small pieces of rounded glass varying in color from light green to black, and of rather unusual composition for a glass. Tektites of various types are found scattered by the thousands over certain limited regions of the earth. Moldavites are a type found in Bohemia and Moldavia, Czechoslovakia. Australites are a variety found scattered over a particular area of two million square miles in southern Australia. The unusual composition of tektite glass, the lack of association with volcanoes and volcanic glass, the fact that the particles are scattered in particular patterns over certain areas, and finally their odd shape—all this suggests an extraterrestrial origin and rapid passage through the atmosphere.

The fall of meteorites has always excited man's imagination—so much so that accurate observation is rarely made. Scientific literature is filled with reports of what people thought they saw rather than what they actually did see. Whenever real or imaginary meteorites fall, they are usually reported as being glowing hot. Later examination, however, sometimes shows that bits of grass pressed to the surface by the impact are not even charred.

Varied specimens result from the sedimentary processes of mineral-bearing solutions. BELOW: *Fossil brachiopod replaced by pyrite, from Ohio.* RIGHT: *Sand inclusions in azurite, from France.* BOTTOM: *Coral replaced by chalcedony, Florida.* FACING: *From Argentina, cross-section slices of rhodochrosite stalactites.*

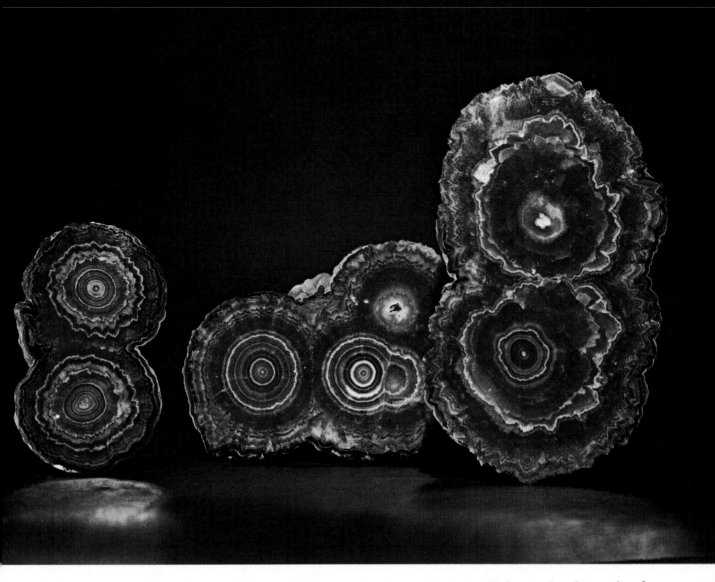

The fact is that meteorites pass through the atmosphere so rapidly that only their surface skin heats up, glows, melts, and sloughs off. The interior does not even have time to warm up from its frigid passage through the incredible cold of space. Freshly fallen meteorites have even been found with a coat of frost formed by condensation of moisture on the cold surfaces.

Perhaps the best-known hole in the world was made by the bullet-like impact of a meteorite: the Canyon Diablo Meteor Crater near Winslow, Arizona. This old crater, formed perhaps thirty or forty thousand years ago, measures almost one mile across the rim and is almost six hundred feet deep. Even after thousands of years of erosion,

the crater remains, and thousands of pounds of scattered meteorite fragments have been recovered from as far as eight miles away from it.

In early 1947, the hot, compressed shock wave of air from a falling meteorite two hundred miles north of Vladivostok, Russia, laid waste many square miles of forest. The blast of air shattered solid rock, tore up large trees and tossed them several miles away, and gouged out dozens of craters, some almost one hundred feet wide and fifty feet deep.

And yet the fall of meteorites may sometimes be gentle. Dr. George P. Merrill, formerly of the Smithsonian, reports in *Minerals from Earth and Sky* an unusual fall near Hessle, Sweden, in 1869, when "The stones fell in great numbers. ... Although so brittle as to be crumbled between the thumb and finger, few were broken by force of impact, and one which fell on the ice rebounded without rupture."

It is not widely realized that there is also, from the heavens, a constant gentle sifting down of the fine ash remains of all the millions of meteorites destroyed by our atmosphere each day. In fact the earth proceeds along its orbit like an enormous vacuum cleaner, sweeping up multitudes of celestial objects.

PSEUDOMORPHS: Petrified wood is very popular these days among amateur gem-cutters, tourist-souvenir manufacturers, collectors, and souvenir

TOP: *The ancient, mile-wide Canyon Diablo meteorite crater, Arizona.* ABOVE: *Meteorite sample sawed for study.* FACING: *Two meteorites, from Antarctica and Mexico, contain olivine and a nickel-iron metal alloy—combinations not found on earth.*

hunters. It is so popular, in fact, that the United States government has set up regulations controlling its removal from federal property.

Petrified wood is extraordinary material. It looks very much like the wood that it once was, which has now been completely replaced by stone. Some of the handsomest petrified wood specimens are found in the Petrified Forest of northern Arizona. Millions of years ago, floods swept these trees down from the hills year after year. In the process the trees were stripped of leaves, bark, roots, and branches, and then buried in muds consisting mostly of volcanic ash. Volcanic ash is rich in quartz, and also contains some iron and manganese. Water, seeping through the mud, dissolved the minerals from the volcanic ash and carried them to the buried tree trunks, where they slowly and delicately permeated the wood spaces. Eventually the minerals entirely replaced the cell structure of the wood, though it was not destroyed in form. Iron and manganese impurities added vivid dashes of bright red, orange, yellow, brown and black. Millions of years later the erosion of the burial grounds gradually brought to light these logs, now forever preserved as brightly colored stone.

It is not only living things like wood that can be replaced by mineral species. Minerals may actually replace each other without a change in external form. Such replacements are called pseudomorphs.

From the moment minerals are produced by one process or another, they are subject to chemical attack and alteration if there is change in their surroundings. Some minerals resist change and are relatively stable. Others change so easily on exposure to heat, light and moisture that it is impossible to preserve them. Changes can be of

several types. The simplest is a loss of part of the mineral's constituents, usually water. Water escapes from some minerals into the air merely on standing. In other minerals, part of the constituents may be removed by the dissolving action of solutions that nature sends flowing by. Constituents may be as easily added as removed by the same solutions.

Sometimes whole groups of a mineral's crystals may be dissolved away, leaving in a rock cavities or molds that preserve their exact shape. Later these holes or molds become filled with quartz, calcite or some other mineral species brought in by solution. This process makes perfect casts of specimens, which have the shape of the orig-

On this and the facing page, a group
of minerals that characteristically
display light and radiation effects.
ABOVE: *Radioactive, fluorescent
autunite from Spokane, Washington.*
RIGHT: *Labradorite from Labrador,
turned* (FAR RIGHT) *to display
schiller.* FACING, LEFT: *Iridescent
limonite from Mexico.* TOP, RIGHT:
*Radioactive curite from the
Congo.* BOTTOM, RIGHT: *Radioactive
uranophane from New Mexico.*

inal mineral but none of the other original characteristics. This explains the origin of their Greek name pseudomorph, *pseudo* meaning false and *morph* meaning shape.

There are many kinds of pseudomorphs known, including precious opal after (which means replacing) glauberite, quartz after fluorite, pyrite after shells and other fossils, clay after feldspar, and malachite after azurite.

LODESTONE: Marco Polo, in accounts of his voyages to ancient China, describes the use of special stones as direction finders. The ancient Chinese knew that certain pieces of iron ore had the ability to align themselves in a certain direction when held in suspension. And by the fourteenth century, when Geoffrey Chaucer men-

tioned lodestones in his "Shipman's Tale," magnets had become an important piece of navigational equipment.

Lodestone—originally lead stone because of its use as a direction finder—is a peculiar variety of the mineral species magnetite, an oxide of iron (Fe_3O_4). It attracts bits of iron and steel with a strange force, which even now is not completely understood. This same force surrounds the entire earth, making our planet itself a very large magnet. It also surrounds any electric wires through which a current is flowing, making it possible to create powerful electromagnets with thousands of coils of wire. These electromagnets are used in turn to endow pieces of iron, steel, and other metal alloys with the same magnetic

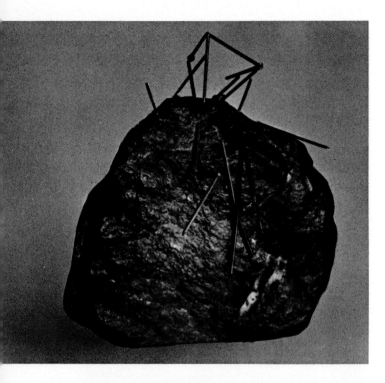

characteristic by exposing them to the strong magnetic force for a period of time.

All minerals are affected in some way by very strong magnets. Some, notably magnetite and pyrrhotite, are strongly attracted by simple iron magnets or by lodestone. These minerals are classed as ferromagnetic. Some are actually repelled by the force and are classed as diamagnetic. Others are attracted to varying degrees, and are classed as paramagnetic.

Because each species is attracted or repelled to a specific degree, it can be magnetically separated in the laboratory, in industrial and mining procedures, and in prospecting. A magnetometer—an instrument that registers variations in the earth's magnetic force—can be carried or flown over large areas to detect the presence of iron-ore deposits by recording variations in the earth's magnetism.

INCLUSIONS: When the Seven Dwarfs placed Snow White in a crystal casket to preserve her from harm, they were duplicating a long-established natural process. Almost every time nature grows a crystal, she encases in it a variety of objects, called inclusions. They are scientifically important because they are evidence of the temperatures, pressures, composition, and other characteristics of the environment in which the mineral formed.

Not only solids but liquids and gases are often trapped during crystal growth. The difference between the white, opaque variety of quartz called milky quartz and the clear, glassy variety called rock crystal is caused by multitudes of tiny bubbles of liquid trapped in milky quartz.

Frequently the inclusions will be of more than one kind, each called a phase. One of the most amazing sights to see under a microscope is the two-phase inclusion of a tiny bit of carbon in one of the liquid-filled cavities found in quartz from Herkimer County, New York. The carbon can be seen jittering around in an erratic dance, bombarded this way and that by the ever-moving liquid molecules. This is called the Brownian Motion, after Robert Brown, the botanist who first reported it in 1827.

THE LIQUID MINERALS: People usually think of petroleum when liquid minerals are mentioned. The fact is that petroleum is not a mineral by our definition, since it evolves from living things through an organic process. However, there are two liquids—one common, one rare—that are actually minerals. The common one is water, a nonmetal, and the rare one is mercury, a metal.

Water, of course, is very familiar in its solid state, either as masses of interlocking crystals (ice) or as accumulations of individual crystals (snow). Perhaps the most interesting and fortunate characteristic of solid water is that it is less dense than liquid water and therefore floats on it. Consider what would happen if water at the surface of a lake froze and sank because it was more dense. Sitting on the bottom, it would soon be covered by more sinking ice. Eventually the whole lake would be filled with solid ice, perhaps never to thaw again. As it is the ice layer floats, insulating the water under it from exposure to the low temperatures of the air above.

Liquid mercury is popularly called quicksilver because of its silver color, and because a globule of the liquid rolls rapidly over any surface without wetting it. Quicksilver is thirteen and a half times as heavy as water. It readily forms solutions, called amalgams, with gold and silver. The dentist takes advantage of this in filling teeth, since silver could never be worked into the cavity in its hard metallic form.

The processing of gold ores also relies heavily on mercury's ability as a solvent. The crushed ore is passed over mercury, the gold in the ore becoming an amalgam with the mercury. The amalgam is then removed and the mercury boiled off, leaving behind a spongy mass of quite pure gold. Mercury's amalgam-forming property was well known to the ancients; Pliny described its use in gilding copper and silver.

Very little liquid mercury is found in nature. Almost all commercial mercury is mined as cinnabar, a compound of mercury and sulfur (HgS). Because it is bright red, cinnabar has been used for centuries as a pigment and is still one of the best. The mercury itself is recovered by roasting the cinnabar and driving off the sulfur.

CATACLYSMIC ROCKS: There are times when portions of the earth's crust are subject to violent disruptions or cataclysms, which may produce unusual objects not formed under ordinary circumstances. Three or four rock relatives of quartz illustrate this kind of occurrence. Perhaps the strangest of these is the fulgurite.

Fulgurites are twig- and branch-like, amorphous structures, some of which are several feet long. They are formed when a bolt of lightning strikes a bed of quartz sand. The quartz is fused by the passage of the high-intensity electrical discharge. If the fulgurite is carefully dug out, it is found to be a perfect glass picture of a highly branched electric spark.

The cataclysmic eruption of volcanoes provides other examples of such mineral wonders. Lava is sometimes full of dissolved gases under pressure. When the pressures are relieved, the lava froths and then solidifies. The result is a glass, related to quartz, that is full of tiny gas bubbles. It is called pumice, and is such a light substance that it will float on water. If the gas bubbles in the solidified froth are quite large, the rock assumes a honeycomb appearance and is called scoria. Scoria, too, is light enough to float.

Even more unusual is Pele's Hair, named after Pele, the Hawaiian goddess of the volcano. Specimens of this lava actually look like silken strands of hair. It is formed when drops of liquid lava are spewed out, stretched, or spun into long glassy hairs, which the wind then tangles together in intricate masses.

The wonders of the mineral kingdom appear limitless. With science and industry pressing for further exploration, and with increasingly sophisticated tools and techniques, it seems likely that earth scientists will frequently be adding many further discoveries to the remarkable phenomena that have already been revealed.

FACING: *Magnetism, shown here in magnetite or lodestone, is a phenomenon not yet fully explored. Lodestone was originally called "lead stone" because of its use as a direction finder, which was already known to the ancient Chinese.*

In Search of Treasure: Classic Sites
5

*Nature jealously guards her riches;
men who want them must endure much
—and have more than a little luck*

Every country of the world has its mining districts, and each of these has its own methods and history. Six of the districts, swinging around the globe from California to Australia, illustrate the variety of man's difficulties as he presses the search for mineral treasure. Each of these areas is a classic site for the recovery of some mineral substance as highly prized in today's brisk commercial trade as it was in centuries past.

SOUTH AFRICA'S DIAMONDS: The Boers, who trekked northward in 1850 to escape the dominant English influence in their original Cape Colony at the tip of South Africa, crossed the Vaal River into the Transvaal to carve out new farms in peace and tranquillity. They found themselves, instead, overrun by the would-be miners of the diamond rush of 1870.

It was triggered when, in 1866, young Erasmus Jacobs found on his father's farm a pretty pebble, which he gave to his sister for a game they called "five stones." This pebble turned out to be a 21.7-carat diamond. Bought by the colony's governor for $25,000, it was displayed in Paris as the Eureka diamond—and the rush was on. Hordes of fortune seekers, fresh from the gold fields of California, Australia, New Zealand, swept into Transvaal seaports and flooded out over the whole area.

At first the Dutch farmers and native Africans fought them off. But as new discoveries were made—among them the 83.5-carat Star of South Africa, another "pebble" picked up downstream from the Jacobs farm—the tide of invaders became overwhelming. The diamond-mining industry had come to stay.

Some of the greatest finds were made by chance. In the crown colony of Griqualand West, a servant boy set to digging as a punishment discovered diamonds on the campsite of the Red Caps, a small prospecting group. Almost overnight, the site became Kimberley—named after Britain's foreign secretary.

Another farm in the territory, bought from the De Beers brothers for $30,000, became the site of a major mine that was eventually to produce a half-billion dollars in diamonds. Diamonds were also found during this period on a farm to the south near Jagersfontein. Soon after, in the bottom of a cattle pond—Du Toits pan—some farmers found a heavy salting of diamonds. All of these occurrences gave their names to the great mines of today—Dutoitspan, Bultfontein, De Beers, Kimberley, Jagersfontein, and Premier.

The diamond mines are located in two kinds of diggings—river gravels and "dry" diggings. The river gravels were the hunting grounds of the first prospectors—from Hopetown, along the Orange River to its junction with the Vaal River, and also up the Vaal as far as the town of Pontcherstroom.

In these locations, diamonds occur because of millions of years of erosion which have torn away thick layers of the surface of Africa. Thousands of feet of surface have been carried off toward the sea, producing extensive deposits of diamond-bearing gravels and ocean-bottom deposits along the coast of Africa.

Later, prospectors found diamonds in dry

PRECEDING PAGES: *An aerial view of a classic in the making—roads outlining the great terraced pit at the Mission Mine, a young open-pit mine in an enormous Arizona body of low-grade copper ore.*

diggings on various farms, most of them on a plateau between the Vaal and Modder Rivers near Kimberley. Here the diamonds are found in deposits of rock of igneous origin called kimberlite, which goes down to considerable depths and is the filling in the necks or pipes of a number of extinct volcanoes.

The deepest mine in any of these pipes is the Kimberley, which goes down 3520 feet. The kimberlite and diamonds here go still deeper, but mining at this great depth becomes uneconomical. The largest of the pipe mines is the Premier, located near Pretoria in the Transvaal. On the surface it covers eighty acres, and it extends to a depth of several hundred feet. The operation at the Premier is quite modern and it will some-

day go down to considerably greater depths.

Most of the pipes are barren of diamonds. Even in the rich pipes, four to six small diamonds in a cubic yard of ore is a good average. Only large-scale mining can work such ores profitably. The original rock of which most of the kimberlite consists is called peridotite, and is composed of the mineral species olivine with some bronzite, chrome diopside, and other substances. At the top of the pipe, exposed to the atmosphere, the kimberlite decomposes and becomes yellowish and crumbles easily.

It was in this "yellow earth" that the first pipe-seated diamonds were found. Hauled out and dumped on "floors"—flat cleared patches of land— the kimberlite weathered and decomposed still

An early nineteenth-century drawing shows basalt columns in Westphalia, Germany, originally upright, tilted by the earth's crustal movement. Lush vegetation springs from the covering of eroded volcanic soil, which is usually rich.

more, and was then crushed and washed to remove clay and other lighter materials. The heavy concentrates that remained were run over a grease table. Diamonds stuck to the grease, while the other minerals were shaken and washed along their way. Later the diamonds were removed, cleaned, and sorted for sale. Almost the entire process was accomplished with hand labor and muscle power.

Eventually, miners reached the bottom of the yellow earth in the pipes and assumed it was the end of the operation. Discovery that there were diamonds in the underlying "blue earth" renewed mining efforts. Blue earth is also peridotite, but unexposed and unweathered to its yellow form. Exposure on the weathering floors remedied this situation.

The history of the most powerful force in today's diamond market—the mammoth De Beers diamond cartel—begins in the diamond rush of 1870. It was the custom of the diggers to make local agreements about their claims. Usually, no man was allowed to operate more than one claim at a time, and a claim was only thirty-one feet square. With miners working on top of each other, the mining areas became a great sea of churned-up earth in various stages of excavation and collapse. Slides and cave-ins, difficulty in moving off the loads of ore, water-seepage problems, and squabbles over conflicting claims created a state of chaos.

Onto this scene came young Cecil Rhodes, eighteen years old. At first he only rented pumps to hold back the troublesome water seepage. But soon he began to buy up claims at the De Beers mine. By the time he was twenty-eight, he was the president of De Beers, and a rich man.

At the Kimberley, an enterprising promoter named Barnett Barnato had gained control and had handled the hazard of great shale slides by sinking tremendous shafts and converting to underground mining. But both Kimberley and De Beers suffered because the financial foundation of the industry was unsteady. Every time floods or slides threatened, the claim holders would panic and sell diamonds to cover anticipated losses, thus ruining the market.

Rhodes and Barnato both felt that a monopoly control of the big mines was necessary to stabilize the market. In the tremendous financial battle that ensued, Rhodes finally won because the Rothschilds were behind him. By 1889 De Beers Consolidated Mines Limited had its monopoly in diamond pipe mines.

During this period, Sir Ernest Oppenheimer appeared on the scene as a diamond buyer, moved into gold mining, and organized, with English and American money, the powerful Anglo-American Corporation. This company wisely began to buy up diamond mines north of the Orange River and alluvial deposits in Alexander Bay. Watching this activity, the De Beers Company in 1926 asked Sir Ernest to become a director. By 1929 he was chairman of the board and had sold the entire Anglo-American diamond operation to De Beers.

Losses through theft at the mines had been another sizable problem; at this time, the Illicit Diamond Buying Act was passed, making it illegal to buy diamonds except from licensed dealers. Also, security-tight compounds were established around the mines. All native laborers were carefully searched before leaving the compounds. With the leakage blocked, the monopoly and control of diamond sources was now complete.

AUSTRALIA'S OPALS: The opal region of south

FACING: *In an ancient Japanese gold mine, the shaft follows the ore vein. Modern shafts go straight down.*

and east Australia is a tremendous spread of uninviting, primitive terrain. Thus far only a handful of opal-producing districts has been found, but there is every promise that more discoveries will be made. Isolation from civilization, lack of water, and almost unbearable temperatures deter most would-be miners. The erratic, unpredictable occurrence of precious opal has prevented development of large-scale mining companies using modern techniques. Thus, the comforts of civilization that usually flow into wealth-producing mining areas have not yet come to the opal diggings of the states of New South Wales, South Australia, and Queensland.

Common opal, with no dazzling display of fire, is found almost everywhere. But precious opal is rarer than diamond. Hungarian opal mines yielded poor-quality gem material for many years, but not until the discovery of Australian opal—a modern occurrence—was the active opal market created that now exists.

All through the accounts of discoveries in Australian opal country there runs a refrain of the unspeakable hardships suffered by early prospectors. Many of the mines are located in the "outback" or the "Never-Never" as it is called locally. This is the region through which, in one place, the Trans-Australian Railroad runs for over three hundred miles in an absolutely straight and flat line and daytime temperatures average over 100 degrees. Only about five inches of rain fall each year. Drinking water must sometimes be transported many miles. Added to all this, the early prospectors and sheepherders were often attacked by the aborigines.

In 1875, the Aladdin Opal Mine was founded in the Thackaringa Hills by an itinerant miner named Paddy Green. Some of his gorgeous flashing opals—locally called "Yowah nuts" because they were first found near the Yowah homestead—were taken to the gem dealers of Hatton Garden in London by a Queensland dealer named Herb Bond. Though London was then the center of the world gem trade, the only opals the dealers had ever seen before were the inferior ones from the old Hungarian mines. Bond's specimens were so good that the dealers were certain they were artificial. He found no buyers.

Meanwhile, new discoveries were made, such as the boulder opal at Quilpie in Queensland. Here the opal occurred as coatings and as filling in fractures in brown boulders of concretionary iron oxide and quartz. Quilpie also produced a number of fine large pieces, the largest of which was a tree limb, found in 1898, which had been replaced by precious opal. Reportedly, this limb measured ten feet long by one foot in diameter. It was unfortunately broken up for cutting.

With only sporadic mining proceeding in the Yowah and other opal fields, the opal market remained limited to Australia. It was in this period that Tully Wollaston, a young surveyor, formed a famous partnership with an Adelaide lawyer, Dave Tweedie. Having obtained financing, Wollaston set out by horseback and camelback across the desolate wastes to find a miner named Joe Bridle, somewhere north of Quilpie, who was rumored to have some fabulous opal. The difficult seven-hundred-mile gamble was successful; Wollaston returned with the gems.

When he took samples to London, in 1889, Wollaston met the same difficulties as Bond had years before. But he finally persuaded Hasluck Brothers to merchandise some cut stones in their shops in London and in Maiden Lane, New York. The venture paid off; the opal's beauty quickly

TOP: *Enormous low-grade deposits in east-central Arizona rock are important United States copper reserves.*
RIGHT: *Native copper from Michigan's Keeweenaw Peninsula, mined by Indians long before Europeans arrived.*

found a market. Demands and orders began to come in. Wollaston and Tweedie now had a firm in operating condition, and the Australian opal industry was launched.

The famous White Cliffs mine got under way when, just short of seven hundred miles northwest of Sydney as the crow flies, a group of kangaroo hunters stumbled on opal in 1889. They brought pieces of the color-flashing stone to the Mining Register in the nearest town, Wilcannia, sixty miles to the southeast. At this point a miner named Ted Murphy entered the picture, helping them to develop their mining operation. Murphy, through his experience at handling opal at White

Cliffs, got to know quality and prices and supply problems as well as anyone in the field. He later joined Wollaston and Tweedie, and eventually became the largest and most talented buyer of opal in Australia.

The first White Cliffs shaft went only to twenty feet because it was believed that this was the bottom of the deposit. Since that time many other and deeper shafts have been opened, much fine opal has been found and sold, and this opal field is now known to be at least five miles long and two miles wide. Many of the mines have exposed opalized shells and other fossilized animal remains. These finds confirm that this part of

Australia, millions of years ago, was a vast ocean basin. Presumably, opal deposits can be found anywhere in the basin. By "miners right," each miner was permitted to cover only one hundred square feet of ground in his operation. It is conceivable that with the persistence of primitive mining techniques, plus the forbidding nature of the country, the entire ancient ocean basin may never be completely searched, mined, or exhausted of its opal.

In the desolate country northeast of White Cliffs, a sheepherder grazing his flock was caught in a sweeping thunderstorm on a small rise. The hill rose only thirty-five feet, but this was suf-ficient for the entire close-packed flock to be wiped out by a single bolt of lightning. From then on the place had a name—Lightning Ridge.

At this spot, near the New South Wales side of the border with Queensland, opal was discovered in 1905. This opal differed from all the other kinds then known because its background color, in which the typical opal fire danced, was so dark. It immediately became known as black opal, and—though Sydney gem dealers rejected it as too dark, and worthless—it was so extraordinary that a flood of miners poured into the area. The short-sighted gem dealers found history and the gem market passing them by; fifty thousand acres of the area have since been declared an official mining field. Actually, less than 5 percent of it is currently being worked.

Mines at Lightning Ridge are typical of those elsewhere in the opal fields. All the work is done with pick and shovel. The shafts go down about twenty-five feet, through gravel, sandstone, and quartzite layers, before the opal-bearing white clay layer is reached. They are about two and a half feet wide by about six feet long, just big enough for a miner to descend and swing a pick. Usually the mine is a two-man operation— one in the shaft and one to hoist the opal-bearing clay up the shaft by windlass and bucket. Sometimes a third and fourth are employed to sift the clay through a screen so that no scrap of opal is lost. "Nobbies"—small round and almond-shaped masses of opal—are the final product. Although the area was discovered in 1915, it is still productive, and as recently as 1946 an aborigine discovered similar opal over eight miles away.

The names Yowah, Quilpie, White Cliffs, Lightning Ridge, and the equally famous Coober Pedy, Eulo, and Tintabar add romance to the

ABOVE: *Open-pit mining was typical of early diamond mines like Kimberley. Here diamonds were found— and are still found—in deposits of rock of igneous origin called kimberlite.*

139

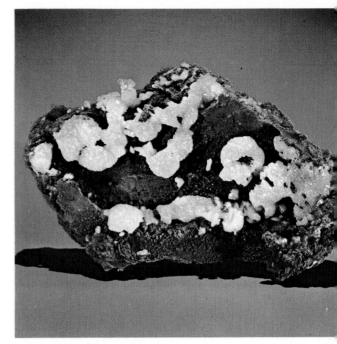

discussion of opal, as Kimberley and De Beers do to diamond. In 1930 two boundary riders, out checking grazing fences, discovered a deposit that added the name Andamooka to this illustrious list. Only one hundred forty miles north of Port Augusta in South Australia, and not too far from the well-known Australian rocket base at Woomera, this has become a productive field.

There is no doubt that this is not the last of the big discoveries. The world market for good opal is large and active and prices have gone up dramatically, a fact that is certain to stimulate the search. Obviously, great portions of the potential opal-producing country in Australia have not been tapped at all and new discoveries are bound to follow.

FRANKLIN ZINC: The Dutch miners who worked the Delaware River Valley for copper ores about 1640 thought they had struck it rich when they got to the place now known as Mine Hill in Sussex County, New Jersey. The exposed brownish-red

ore looked like the copper ores they knew so well. Mine workings were established by about 1650, but that was the last heard of the Dutch copper ventures at that location. For reasons that the Dutch didn't understand and that were not to be cleared up for another one hundred fifty years, the red ore yielded no copper.

The area later passed into the hands of William Alexander—who preferred to be known as Lord Stirling though his claim to the title had been denied, apparently because of his active role as an American Revolutionary officer. Like the Dutch, he tried to make use of the red ore, and sent a shipment of it to England to be smelted. The smelting never took place, but the shipment probably accounts for certain specimens found in old mineral collections in England. Undaunted, Lord Stirling erected his own furnace at Franklin, hoping to smelt his plentiful black material, thought to be iron ore. The furnace never smelted any ore and in time fell into ruins.

By 1816, when the property came into the hands of Dr. Samuel Fowler, there was strong evidence that the Mine Hill ores just weren't copper and iron. But what were they? Samples of them, making their way about the scientific community, were examined with curiosity, interest, and no conclusions.

The mystery was solved in the first volume of the *American Mineralogical Journal*, published in 1814. In an article entitled "Description and Chemical Examination of an Ore of Zinc from New Jersey," the red-brown mineral, zincite, was shown to be an ore of zinc and not of copper.

This paper was only the first of many. For years Dr. Fowler and his son encouraged scientists to continue studying the materials that were being recovered from the mines. A steady stream of mineralogists was entertained by the Fowlers and given specimens for study. The names of many important mineralogists here and abroad have appeared on a long line of scientific papers, which have been published steadily since Fowler's time.

Dr. Fowler tried repeatedly to exploit the deposits commercially, but it seemed hopeless. In 1850, control of the property passed on to the New Jersey Zinc Company. A number of mines sprang up, which in 1897 were consolidated and modernized. The Palmer Shaft, fifteen hundred feet deep, was sunk to the base of the ore body, and from that time all ore from everywhere in the ore body was brought up through this shaft.

Actually, there are two ore bodies. One is at Mine Hill near the town of Franklin, the other three miles away near the town of Ogdensburg. Both are very extensive and are shaped in enormous troughs, rather like the two ends of a canoe. The geological origin of the ores is still somewhat controversial. It must have been a unique combination of geologic events, because there are no other deposits like them anywhere in the world. They sit in a region of coarsely crystalline white marble or limestone called Franklin Limestone. In the limestone itself are some unusually fine mineral specimens for the collector. None of these contains zinc or manganese, which is strange since the ore bodies are rich in both. The Franklin Limestone itself has been mined commercially.

At first the ore seems very simple in composition. Seventy percent is made up of the minerals franklinite (an oxide of zinc, iron and manganese), willemite (a zinc silicate), and zincite (a zinc oxide). Twenty-five percent is calcite, calcium carbonate. The remaining 5 percent is an extremely numerous and interesting suite of well over one hundred fifty different species. Many of these were first discovered at Franklin; many are not known anywhere else in the world, and much of the material has yet to be identified. Among the recognized minerals are very rare lead silicates— margarosanite, barysilite, nasonite, roeblingite, and larsenite.

Investigation of these minerals has now extended over almost a century and a half. Many collections have been made of Franklin specimens all during the operation of the mines. Most of the important ones are in major mineral museums, still available for study.

These remarkable ores have been put to many uses. Franklinite, the most abundant, can be separated easily from the rest of the ores because it is magnetic and can be pulled out of the crushed mixture. The franklinite is then converted to white zinc oxide and to spiegeleisen. Zinc oxide is used as a nonstaining whitener in paints and in the manufacture of certain rubber

Australia, not fully exploited, remains a promising hunting ground. ABOVE: *The 1851 gold rush drew hopefuls from around the world.* RIGHT: *At famous Lightning Ridge, an expert cuts and polishes an opal.* FACING: *Sapphire-bearing gravel is screened at Rubyvale in Queensland.*

products. Spiegeleisen is an iron-manganese alloy used, especially in the Bessemer process, for making manganese steels. The willemite and zincite from the ores are kept together during ore separation and end up as spelter, or crude zinc, for use in various industries.

As the Franklin ores were worked, it was discovered that some of them were fluorescent, glowing in bright colors under ultraviolet light. This permitted easy separation of the waste material from the ores by hand, on picking tables, as it came out of the mine. The need for better methods of producing ultraviolet light specifically for this purpose so stimulated research that it led eventually to the present line of excellent light sources now available to industry and collectors.

The half upcurving mass of ore at Mine Hill, known earlier as Franklin Furnace and now commonly as Franklin, has been mined out and operations are closed down. However, over in Sparta Township the mine is in full operation. The story of the resistant Dutch "copper ores" is far from fully told.

CALIFORNIA'S GOLD: The United States still has vast hoards of gold—in the ground where nature put it. Mine operators insist that far more gold remains in California, awaiting mining, than has already been dug out of the ground there.

There had been sporadic discoveries of gold in many parts of California before 1848, when it was still part of Mexico. Indians would occasionally bring samples to the Spanish missions. Richard Henry Dana, in his biographical *Two Years Before the Mast*, wrote that every ship calling at West Coast ports would bring gold dust back to the East. Of course, the territory belonged to Mexico, but when the Mexican War ended in 1848 with the Treaty of Guadalupe Hidalgo, which gave California to the United States, the lid was off.

The pot had almost boiled over prematurely. Just ten days earlier, gold had been found where a man named John Sutter was building a mill. As workman after workman found additional samples, word traveled, and nearby towns were depopulated by a stampede to the area. The news spread to the Oregon Territory, Mexico, South America, and abroad—and the tremendous rush of gold seekers toward California was under way.

Reaching California, the new settlers found an undeveloped wilderness with no government, no laws, no taxes, no comforts—but with unlimited opportunity. They fanned out along a two-hundred-mile stretch in the Sierra Nevada mountains and set up their mining claims and tent communities on the slopes. Many struck it rich quickly—some by accidental discovery, others by very hard work.

Most of the gold was recovered by panning: separating the gold from the sands and gravels by washing with water. The heavy gold settled out and the lighter waste material was carried off. The panning was often done right in the stream beds. Where gravels were mined and washed at some distance away from the streams, long ditches were dug to bring the water to them.

A standard item of equipment was the "rocker," a three-foot-long box set on rockers, with wooden cleats nailed at intervals on the inside bottom.

THIS PAGE: *Agate, a fine-grained quartz, forms from ground water seeping through rock cavities. Its color variations result from impurities that change as the solutions forming each layer accumulate.* CENTER, RIGHT: *This specimen is from Rio Grande do Sul, Brazil; all others on this page are from Central Mexico.*

144

Gold-bearing sand was shoveled in at one end, while a current of water ran through it. The heavy gold sank and settled on the cleats; the lighter gravel was washed along and out the other end. Sometimes, to give the gold a longer distance in which to settle, the rocker was abandoned for a "long tom." This was a long trough, or several joined together, with no rockers but with a similar series of cleats in the bottom.

Hydraulic mining techniques lightened some of the backbreaking labor. Water, impounded in reservoirs, was released through pipes in high-pressure jets against the gravel deposits, tearing them apart to wash out the gold. "Booming" was also practiced: sudden release of the dammed-up water so that its onslaught tore out the gravels. These methods were actually destructive of land; eventually, both practices were controlled by law after much terrain and even some towns had been destroyed by their ravages.

All told, California has produced between two and three billion dollars in gold. About two-thirds of this has come from placer mining in the gravels. The other third came from the original gold veins in the mother lode. Usually the original occurrence of this gold is in white or gray quartz veins, which cut through the slates of the Sierra Nevadas in great numbers. Erosion of these veins, especially on the west slopes toward the sea, has been going on for as much as seventy million years, spreading vast accumulations of gold-bearing gravels down the slopes. Some of these gravels were later covered by lava flows. The mother lode extends approximately one hundred twenty miles from near Georgetown to Mariposa.

Gold recovery today, from both placer and hard-rock mining, is considerably more efficient than it was in the early days. Large-scale operations with power machinery and carefully engineered procedures have cut the mining costs sharply by increasing productivity. Better extraction methods have also been developed. The gold can be removed from its crushed ores by the use of liquid mercury, in the amalgam method described in Chapter 4. Another method involves treating the finely crushed ore with solutions of sodium or potassium cyanide. The gold dissolves out of the ore. Zinc metal is added to the resulting gold solution and the gold comes out again free of the waste material in the ore.

It is only through improved methods, reduced costs, and the value of other metals sometimes associated with gold that any mines at all continue to operate in the United States. At the onset of World War II, the War Production Board ruled that gold mining was nonessential, and thousands of mines were shut down. Attempting to resume operations after the war, mine operators found that extensive refurbishing of dilapidated machinery and mine workings was necessary. Meanwhile, the cost of labor and materials, transportation, power, taxes, consultant fees, and marketing costs had gone up significantly, while the price of gold was still kept at the 1934 level.

It costs more to mine most of the gold deposits of the United States than the gold itself is worth. Since 1934 the dollar is exactly equal in value to one thirty-fifth of an ounce of gold, by law. It costs more than that in labor, equipment, engineering, and other expenses to find the ore, take it from the ground, extract the gold and sell it. The result is that thousands of once productive gold mines are idle, and ghost mining towns dot the West.

Meanwhile, as our cheap gold flows out to the rest of the world, the demand for gold within

KEEWEENAW COPPER: It was 1783 ... and the time had come for the signing of the Treaty of Paris, ending the American Revolutionary War. Benjamin Franklin, an astute bargainer, had heard somehow that the Indians had been mining copper on Isle Royale in Lake Superior. Sensing a profitable opportunity, he delayed the signing of the treaty until the island was made part of the United States.

He was wiser than he knew. The famous copper deposits of Lake Superior lie on the island and on the Keeweenaw Peninsula, which is a tongue of Michigan land jutting out sixty miles from the south shore of the lake. On it, copper is found in a four-mile-wide belt running for almost one hundred miles. This deposit of copper is unique in the world because the ore mineral is native copper itself and not one of the various minerals of copper in combination with something else, as usually found.

Geologically, the story of this mining district begins over five hundred million years ago, when serious earth disturbances caused lava to well up through great cracks in the crust of the earth where Lake Superior is now. Steam bubbled up through the lava, making it rather frothy at the top. When cooling eventually solidified the molten, bubbly rock, a thick porous layer was left covering the region. The steam holes left in this rock are called amygdules. Continued strong disturbances then tilted the lava rock layers, making them more nearly vertical.

A few million years later hot solutions, rich in copper, came up from below. Their load of copper was deposited in the frothy rock, filling the holes and cracks in the tilted lava beds. Mines have followed down the slopes of these amygdaloidal rock beds for as much as two miles. At this depth

the United States is rising. As its price remains steady against the rising prices of other metals, its decorative qualities, as well as its good electrical properties, are increasingly attractive to craftsmen and to industry. Drawing on the diminishing gold supply to satisfy these uses drains the government reserve at a rate rapidly approaching one hundred million dollars a year.

What the United States needs is a new discovery of bonanza—from the Spanish, meaning fair weather—ore that can be scooped out of the ground in large quantities.

TOP: *Early pick-and-shovel miners flocked to California when gold was found at Sutter's Mill.* CENTER: *Workman James Marshall, who made the discovery.* FACING: *Modern prospectors scuba-dive for gold in California's Yuba River.*

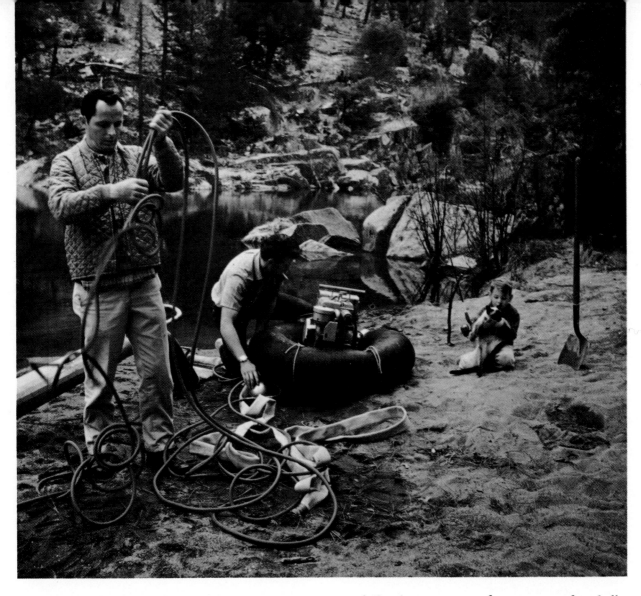

mining becomes too costly; the copper, however, has been traced on downward to at least twenty thousand feet. Altogether the district has produced almost nine billion pounds of copper, to say nothing of large amounts of silver and other rare metals as by-products.

The development of electric street cars, and the spreading use of electricity, gave the Michigan copper industry its greatest boost. Copper is a better conductor of electricity than any metal except silver, and can be drawn into wire without breaking, so that it is ideal for many electrical applications. Also, since more than 80 percent of the alloys brass and bronze consists of copper, it has valuable alternate use. In wartime the demand for copper skyrockets because of the increased

need for brass to manufacture cases for shells.

No one knows when man first found the outcroppings of glistening copper metal in the Lake Superior region, or began to find uses for the pieces he chipped off. The discoverers must have been some prehistoric Indians of the area, for evidence has been found of ancient fires, apparently used to detach the copper from its rock. Many primitive copper tools have also been recovered.

The first published account of the Keeweenaw copper appeared in Paris in 1636, in which Jesuit missionaries, the first white men in the area, reported that Indians were mining the metal. In 1771 an Englishman, Alexander Henry, attempted unsuccessfully to mine. His travel memoirs in 1809

RIGHT: *The Red Cloud Mine in Yuma County, Arizona, produced wulfenite specimens of special interest to collectors.*
BELOW: *Molten sulfur, pumped up by the Frasch process, fills a cooling vat at a sulfur mining plant in Louisiana.*

mention a large mass he had seen sitting on the bank of the Ontonagon River, near its mouth. It seemed out of place. It is quite possible that it had been moved by its early Indian miners to the river bank from the Minnesota Mine only two miles away in the Ontonagon district. In 1843 the mass was eventually floated down the river on a raft by Julius Eldred. Later it was seized by the United States government and shipped to the city of Washington. Eldred was paid $5664.98 for his expenses and trouble. Finally the sixty-five hundred pound mass, measuring three feet six inches by three feet eight inches, was transferred to the Smithsonian Institution.

The Minnesota Mine, from which the mass might have come, was known for its extraordinarily large masses of copper. One discovered in 1857 measured forty-six feet long by eighteen and a half feet wide and eight and a half feet thick in its largest dimensions. Its weight was recorded at four hundred twenty tons. Twenty men took fifteen months to cut it up, and got twenty-seven tons of chips from the cutting. Incredibly, it was cut in the usual way with three-quarter-inch bladed chisels and hammers. At the time, it was estimated that every square foot of the faces of the cuts cost twelve dollars.

Commercial mining at Keeweenaw did not resume for many years after Alexander Henry gave up. In 1843, the territory was finally ceded to the United States government by the Chippewa Indians. Slowly, monetary speculation and actual mining began in the copper country. By 1853, ten years out of Chippewa hands, the copper mines netted $1,328,406 for their owners.

T. A. Rickard in his *Copper Mines of Lake Superior*, published in 1905, reports that there were thirty-eight different nations represented by the miners at the Calumet and Hecla Mine. There was a "conglomeration of churches" and an "amygdaloid of saloons" in the town. Nationalities did not mix too well; at the Wolverine Mine Englishmen used one end of the changing room and Italians another. In the second room, Austrians used one end and Finns the other. The immigrants from the Cornwall, England, tin mines were considered the best and toughest miners. The Finns were good, too, though they tended to be classified by the mine operators as the "temperance Finns" and the "others."

All of this sounds like familiar echoes of other mining camps all over the world. And yet the mining story of Michigan copper country is actually quite different from many others. There was no sudden discovery, no stampede of prospectors and do-it-yourself miners, no lawlessness or undue hardship in a barren wilderness. With relatively few problems, a wealth of metal was recovered, fortunes were made, and a valuable resource developed.

THE CITY OF GEMS: Five hundred years before the coming of Christ, invaders swept upon the beautiful island of Ceylon. They drove the native Veddhas, probable direct descendants of local Stone Age men, into the jungles before them. Within two hundred years the Sinhalese invaders had created on Ceylon great cities, vast temples, a wondrous civilization.

Then, in a twinkling, it was all gone. Under new, repeated invasions, which destroyed the temples and cities, the Sinhalese were driven to the southern part of the 25,332-square-mile island. Here in their southern stronghold, these people now mine all the gemstones for which Ceylon is justly famous.

Mining is centered in the districts of Ratnapura,

Balangoda, and Rackwana. Ratnapura City (city-of-gems in Sinhalese) sits in a wide hollow, nestling among vegetation-covered hills—a breathtaking tropical setting. The highest part of the island rises sharply from a narrow coastal plain in the south to higher ground, and thence all the way to mountain peaks as high as seventy-five hundred feet.

These mountains are part of the very ancient rocks underlying the island, which have been eroding for hundreds of millions of years—an erosion that has covered much of the rock in the highlands with a layer of reddish clay, making rich soil for the rubber and tea plantations in the hills. Seasonally, heavy tropical rains carry off quantities of this cover in rushing red torrents down deep V-shaped river valleys. Gradually the valleys have built thick layers of sediment; bot-

tom land has been covered with as much as twenty feet of overburden. The rich red muds of the land around Ratnapura are completely covered by rice paddies, some of which have undoubtedly been cultivated for a thousand years. Under these paddies lie the gemstones of Ceylon.

Mining is very primitive. A miner and his crew lease a spot in a rice paddy to begin operations. All the land here suffers from the complex, highly subdivided ownership, so the miner's location is more likely determined by the lease he is able to obtain than by some good geological reason. A pit is sunk into the clay some ten to twenty feet deep. To hold back the mud, vertical poles are driven against the walls of the pit, and sticks, branches and palm leaves are wedged behind them. Water, however, gets through this, and the pit must be bailed constantly to keep it from flooding. Discarded gasoline tins are popular bailing implements. Baskets of clay and cans of water are passed up to the surface and dumped continuously until the bottom of the clay layer is reached. All of this work is so arduous, wet, and tropically warm that the men work naked except for loincloths.

Under the clay the iliam, or layer of gem-bearing gravel, is found. Normally it is not very thick, but often it contains rough gem pebbles. All of the gravel is hoisted in bamboo baskets and carried to a nearby stream or water supply to wash off the mud. An expert examiner then carefully hand-sorts the baskets of gravel, and extracts every piece of any potential value. Most of the gravel consists of whitish quartz pebbles, some iron-bearing concretions, and organic matter. However, it also yields an amazing array of gemstones.

There is no greater variety of gems found in any deposit in the world. The sorter is likely to find sapphire of all colors in greatest abundance. There may also be ruby, chrysoberyl, spinel, zircon, topaz, garnet, tourmaline, quartz, moonstone, sphene, cordierite, fibrolite, andalusite, diopside, kornerupine, apatite, sinhalite—a rich variety. Moonstone is the one gem that has actually been found still in the original rocks, others having been found only in the iliam.

The little groups of Sinhalese digging in the clay manage to recover each year gems totaling several hundred thousand dollars. Because of the difficulty of obtaining sufficient land rights for large-scale earth-moving and drainage operations, mining in this area will undoubtedly retain its primitive state. We may never know the full extent of the riches that more sophisticated mining methods might reveal in this country.

Copper mining at Chuquicamata, Chile, near the mountainous edge of the arid Atacama Desert. The half-million tons of overburden—waste—being blasted out of the ore body will be carried off to dumping grounds out of the way.

151

Mineral Masterpieces
6

*Classic mineral specimens, like
great works of art, achieve their
status through experts' judgments*

If a painting by Rembrandt were suddenly reported missing from its honored place in a great museum, the fact would be headlined in newspapers around the world. Police departments, detective agencies, and government offices would all be involved in trying to recover the missing treasure. The theft of important gemstones brings the same reaction, particularly if it is the property of an international personality or one of the world's elite collectors—and, apart from museums, who else can aspire to ownership of such gems? When the celebrated Star of India was lifted recently from the Museum of Natural History in New York, the whole world followed with eager interest the chase and eventual capture of the ingenious perpetrators. Gems are famous, beautiful, valuable, and generally well protected; evidently this makes the audacious gem theft the kind of caper that captures everyone's imagination.

Unique mineral specimens ought to share the same response. They too are exceptional, valuable, protected, and in certain circles even famous. And yet reaction to the theft of important mineral specimens is usually a quiet affair. When the second-largest uncut diamond crystal in the world on public exhibition was stolen from Harvard University a few years ago, it created hardly a ripple. It was a routine police case of theft. Odder still, a couple of years later when the largest uncut diamond crystal on exhibition was stolen from the British Museum, it was even less of a news item. At present, the largest uncut diamond crystal on exhibition is a 254-carat octahedron in the Smithsonian Institution. It is the only large one left, so if it should be stolen its theft might possibly break into print.

The discrepancy in the impact between the loss of a great art treasure and a mineral treasure is strange indeed. Large, well-formed diamond crystals are far rarer than Rembrandt's paintings and just about as irreplaceable. The difference seems to be that mineral museums are relatively poverty-stricken; there is little competition among them for very rare and very expensive items. This keeps prices from being pushed to the heights achieved by paintings and other art works, which are inflated by the competition between wealthy art museums and art collectors.

Most great institutional collections of art throughout the world have their highlyprized old masters. If the collection specializes in modern works it will contain art that, in the best judgment of its curators, will become the classics of the future.

Exact parallels can be drawn with the important mineral museums. All the fine old collections have their classic items—outstanding specimens discovered in former years. New mineral museums, beginning without the foundation of an old gift collection heavy in classics, will attempt to acquire the best of the newly mined specimens. And in the future many of these new specimens will become the rare, hard-to-get, and relatively expensive mineral classics.

Very good mineral specimens of any kind are quite rare. There are reasons for this rarity. For one thing, nature just doesn't produce very many

PRECEDING PAGES: *These newly found specimens meet classic standards. Clockwise from far left: scolecite, muscovite, from Brazil; marcasite from Wisconsin; wulfenite from Mexico.*

extraordinary items. Even when they do exist in a mine or quarry, the obstacles still to be faced before they are carefully preserved in some collection are almost insurmountable. One hundred years ago there was more chance of their being preserved at the mine, since much of the mining was then done by hand, without heavy machinery and powerful explosives. There is nothing more destructive to crystallized specimens than the shock wave of a confined explosion. Also, with the introduction of heavy, expensive machinery and highly organized mining methods, most companies are concerned that the flow of operations may be disrupted by miners' taking time to gather specimens. Some mines control collecting activities by decreeing immediate dismissal for any miner found collecting or selling specimens. This has a definite effect on decreasing the flow of good specimens to collectors and museums—though it never cuts it off completely.

There is a saying among collectors that many thousands more of the good specimens go to the crushers and the mills than ever fall into the hands of collectors and museums. Some mining companies have helped improve the situation by permitting collecting by miners "on their own time" as a sort of fringe benefit. Others have permitted retired miners to bolster their incomes through the collection and sale of specimens. Whatever the mechanism, there is a continual small trickle of specimens from the mines.

Once out of the mine and into the hands of a collector, however, there is still no guarantee that the specimen will survive. When either the miner or the collector transports the specimen from an inaccessible mine to civilization, there is the ever-present possibility that it will suffer irreparable damage, thus perishing as an important

specimen. Having arrived at the collection, there is again no guarantee of its survival. Through ignorance of proper methods for trimming or cleaning, or through carelessness in handling, the specimen can be lost in an instant. Even supposing that it survives and is carefully guarded during the collector's lifetime, it may face eventual destruction. His heirs, through neglect, lack of interest, or mishandling during packing, can easily decrease or destroy its value as a collector's item.

Rembrandt's drawing of a woman and child is a masterpiece far beyond the reach of the average collector. Exceptional old mineral specimens, particularly from worn-out sources, are similarly unique and unavailable—classics of their kind.

Assuming that our specimen is tough enough to have survived all this, and is deposited with a collection, it may face other hardships. Libraries, local schools, historical societies, universities, and banks across the crountry have been recipients of collections. By and large, the care given them is minimal. The country is strewn with collections that were obviously important at one time and are now practically worthless. The chances of survival, then, from the mine to a secure final resting place in a well-cared-for and stable museum collection, are slim indeed.

But among the survivor specimens will be a few that are the finest of their species. The more outstanding the specimen, the better its chances, for it is likely through the years to get consistently good care. Some will be the largest crystals of their kind. Others may have the most unusual color for their species. Still others become important because the mineral deposit they came from is now exhausted and no similar deposits have been found.

The best places to see the old classics are at large museums that have been in the mineral-collecting business for many years. The mineral museums of the United States are relatively young compared to those of Europe. However, some have assumed classical status, like American art museums, through purchases of old collections and through valuable gifts. Many fine modern collections will not drift to museums for perhaps another fifty years or so. Usually, therefore, mineral museums are blessed with old classics but lack a sampling of new ones. This is a typical picture of most mineral museums in the world, except for a very small number that have won a share of new discoveries by developing aggressive solicitation and purchase programs.

Collectors and museums concentrating on the acquisition of fine, newly discovered specimen material are in the same position as those collecting contemporary art. Contemporary art is relatively inexpensive and a bit of a gamble. No contemporary artist is likely to get a million dollars for one painting. Similarly, contemporary mineral specimens are less expensive than old ones, but they are a less speculative investment than modern art, since their beauty, quality, rarity, and general desirability are more obvious. Important new finds are recognized at once. They are—or will be—the new classics.

It would be a mistake, for instance, for the collector to avoid buying superb specimens of calcite from Mexico because they are presently common and cost only between one and ten dollars. Their future will very likely follow the precedent set by the famous calcite specimens from England that were so common twenty-five or thirty years ago, which sold at that time for similar low prices. Now, quality English calcite specimens are just about unavailable at any price.

What are these mineral "Rembrandts"? And how are they recognized? It is a simple matter to buy a color-illustrated catalog of the paintings of almost any great artist, complete with biographical information. Such guides do not exist for mineral specimens. Collectors and museum curators, through comparison of collections and continual shop talk, have passed information along to each other, but only in bits and pieces. The museums themselves are the only catalogs.

Visitors to museums can usually be sure that the finest specimens in the collection will be displayed and that among them will be many classics. To the alert visitor, making comparisons from museum to museum, certain repetitions become

Museum-quality classics like these are obtainable now by trade or transfer; rarely bought. TOP, LEFT: *Tourmaline from Elba, Italy.* TOP, RIGHT: *Stibnite, Ichinokawa, Japan.* LEFT: *Realgar, Transylvania, Rumania.*

evident. Each collection will probably have fat, light blue crystals of topaz from Russia; long, splendent, metallic shafts of stibnite from Japan; and black, opaque, shiny tourmaline groups from Pierrepont, New York. These are some of the classics.

The difficulty lies in retaining exact mental pictures of these specimens while comparing various collections. Also, as mentioned before, most museums possess only old occurrences. This is one potential pitfall for the collector. His idea of what is classic and important may become distorted. He may hunger after the unobtainable old things in the museums while ignoring the new. The new specimens seem too inexpensive to be important, they are too plentiful, everyone has them and, worst of all, they have not been immortalized by descriptions in mineral textbooks or by the occasional publication of photographs in mineralogical literature. Some of them are described below and pictured throughout this book to encourage the collector. There is good reason to anticipate that one day these presently available specimens will be "Rembrandts" along with the old classics.

Appreciation of the classics by the general museum visitor and mineral collector depends chiefly on three things. First, there must be a sensitivity to beauty, since for many of the pieces this is the major claim to fame. There must also be an awareness of the natural history of mineral specimens. For example, the rough, blocky crystals of andalusite from Delaware County, Pennsylvania, are hardly objects of beauty, but they are some of the largest and best-formed groups ever found. Finally, an ability to compare specimens and to discriminate among them is indispensable. To the uninitiated, the specimens in a mineral exhibit are all interesting or all beautiful or all the same—at first. They wonder what the experienced collector sees as he moves slowly through the exhibition, carefully examining each piece. Of course, he is making mental comparisons between these specimens and others he has seen. He is also memorizing details—he may actually take notes—of old classics, which will teach him how to recognize and search out new classics for his own collection.

As an indication of what the collector may want on his "desiderata" list, a very small sampling is given here, listed in the chemical groupings featured in most modern systems of mineralogy. Famous old classics are included, along with some sparkling newcomers. A complete description of classics from even one group could be a volume in itself. Almost every specimen pictured in this book might well be included among the new and old classics.

NATIVE ELEMENTS: Native elements are those that are found free in nature. Both metallic and nonmetallic elements among the minerals are well represented by superb specimens. Of the nonmetals, *sulfur* is the most attractive. The best examples, still available, come from the mines at Agrigento, Cianciana, and elsewhere in Sicily. Bright, clear yellow crystals from microscopic size to four or five inches across occur in homogeneous groups, or associated with outstanding, shiny, white, chisel-pointed crystals of celestite or large, hexagonal, barrel-shaped crystals of aragonite. Some of the new specimens, from San Felipe

in Baja California, are as bright, colorful, and well formed as Sicilian sulfur, even though the crystals do not exceed half an inch.

The best specimens of *diamond*, another nonmetal, have come from South Africa. It is still possible to obtain, at a good price, sharp, transparent octahedrons as loose, single crystals of various sizes. However, good-quality crystals that measure half an inch or larger are almost prohibitive in price for most collectors. Because of newer mining methods, using powerful explosives and large earth-moving machinery, it is often impossible to obtain crystals still embedded in rock. In fact in most of the old specimens of this kind found in museums the crystals have been glued in, although both diamond crystal and rock are

FACING: *Brown siderite rhombs make quartz from Allevard, France, a classic item.* ABOVE: *Large gold nuggets rarely persist intact. One of the largest known is this eighty-two ounce specimen from a California placer mine.*

genuine. Well-shaped, tan diamond crystals in various forms, measuring three-eighths of an inch or more, but not of gem quality, have been obtained from the Congo.

Silver specimens in sheets, wires, and very sharp crystals occur in calcite in the rich ores at Kongsberg, Norway. The beautifully twisted, sculptured, thick wires can be as much as a foot long and as thick as a man's wrist. From the copper mines on the Keeweenaw Peninsula in Michigan the best silver specimens recovered tend to be branching, heavy, fernlike growths of fairly distinct crystals associated with copper. The *copper* specimens from these mines are the finest in the world. They can be obtained in almost any size, all of high quality. Some are aggregates of crystals, one inch or larger, clustered like walnuts in branching groups. Others may be delicate branching fans of coppery fern fronds. Remarkably good copper specimens have appeared in recent years from the New Cornelia Pit at Ajo, Arizona. These, too, have been found in small and large aggregates of one-inch crystals and as branching tree-like growths, all of bright coppery color.

Gold is found in many places and in large specimens. Perhaps the most attractive have been found in California and in Rumania. From the mother-lode country of California have come the finest crystallized specimens. The specimen of flat clustered crystals in the Cranbrook Institute, from the Red Ledge Mine in California, is perhaps the finest gold specimen in the world. Many large nuggets of attractive form have been found also in placer deposits in California. Specimens come from Rumania, as well; these tend to be lighter in color because of the presence of some silver.

Platinum, another noble metal, is rarely found anywhere in its original rock deposits. Extraordinary nuggets, some weighing many ounces, have been found in gravel. The very large rounded nuggets occurring in the headwaters of the Tura River in Perm Province in Russia are the best known. Similar nuggets, almost indistinguishable from their Russian counterparts, come from the Department of Cauca in Colombia.

A few years ago the mineral *allemontite* might have been considered scientifically interesting, but hardly a very desirable show species. The original material, from Allemont in France, was dull and gray. However, this natural arsenic-antimony alloy has since been found at Moctezuma in Sonora, Mexico. The Sonora specimens are bright,

shiny, rounded, colloform masses, which make very attractive additions to a collection.

SULFIDES: Many of the mineral ores from which commercial metals are extracted are classified chemically with the sulfides. As expected, then, mining activities have turned up extraordinarily good specimens of several sulfide minerals. The silver sulfide, *argentite*, is not a beautiful mineral, but like all silver minerals, is rather rare. When well crystallized, it becomes a collector's item. Flattened and malformed and sometimes skeletal crystals and groups of crystals from Arispe in Sonora, Mexico, are highly desirable. Parallel and stacked crystal dendrites, as well as crystals up to an inch or more, from the Freiberg District in Saxony, Germany, are also among the best.

The copper sulfide, *chalcocite*, is best known from two occurrences. In the United States, fine groups of crystals, tarnished black, were found near Bristol, Connecticut; some are still circulating in private collections. More, and perhaps

FACING, TOP: *New painting classics, like this Picasso, are widely catalogued. But mineral classics of comparable stature are not similarly recorded.* LEFT: *Mexican tourmaline, one of many uncatalogued classics.* ABOVE: *Buergerite—found only in San Luis Potosí, Mexico.*

better, specimens have come from Redruth in Cornwall, England. These occurred as hexagonal-looking black plates, often stacked on each other in piles, with some of the crystals as much as an inch in diameter.

One of the commonest lead sulfides, found in many places in excellent specimens, is *galena*. The lead-zinc mines in the Tri-State area of the United States—which includes the corners of Missouri, Kansas and Oklahoma—produce good specimens by the ton. Most of them are in bright, shiny, well-formed cubes, but some are malformed, elongated, or skeletal. Almost any form or variation possible with galena crystals can be found among these specimens. In some of the most attractive, the galena cubes are dusted with a sparkling coat of tiny golden marcasite and pyrite crystals.

The crowning glory of the sulfide division of a collection will be *stibnite* from Japan. This is an antimony sulfide formerly found at Saijo in Iyo Province, on the island of Shikoku. Crystals

in these groups are up to two feet long and some are three inches across. Many are a shiny, steely gray, and are very well formed. They are so magnificent compared to even fine stibnite specimens from other places that they are instantly recognizable. One of the best of these in the United States is in the collection at Bryn Mawr College outside Philadelphia.

Pyrrhotite, an iron sulfide, is still available in classic specimens from at least two occurrences. The mines at Trepca, Yugoslavia, have been producing good specimens for years. Many of the old classic pyrrhotite specimens came from Mexico. These were not available for many years, but new ones are beginning to appear from mines in Chihuahua. Trepca has supplied hexagonal-looking crystal plates up to four inches across, which are usually stacked or arranged in rosettes. The Mexican crystal tend to be more sharply formed and thicker, although not so large in diameter. Both in Yugoslavia and in Mexico, they occur with an attractive bronze tarnish.

SULFOSALTS: The sulfosalts normally occur with sulfides in ore deposits, and are just a little more complex than sulfides in composition, having some antimony or arsenic along with the usual sulfur content. The silver sulfosalts are among the most coveted. Of these, *proustite*—called "ruby silver" by collectors for its red color—is the most attractive. At its best occurrence, in the Dolores Mine at Chanarcillo, Chile, it has been found in bright red single crystals, two to three inches long. It also occurs as larger dendritic groups of crystals. An extraordinarily large mass of proustite crystals is in the collection at the Harvard Mineralogical Museum. Sometimes proustite is so clear that it can be faceted as gemstones, even though the stones are much too soft for any practical use. Ruby silver specimens command prices many times the value of the silver that they contain.

Specimens of *tetrahedrite* are easily recognized by the collector, because they are often sharply crystallized in the tetrahedron crystal form from which the species gets its name. The most attractive of these are crystals from Clausthal in the Harz region of Germany. Crystals up to one inch on an edge are completely coated with a gilding of chalcopyrite, which emphasizes their form and gives color to the blackish crystals. Small but bright and sharply developed crystals associated with pyrite and bournonite on white calcite have been coming in recent times from the Concepción del Oro area in Zacatecas, Mexico.

HALIDES: The halides are minerals containing the elements fluorine, chlorine, bromine, or iodine in their compositions. Two of them, *halite* and *fluorite*, are very common. Halite, sodium chloride, is salt. Salt crystals, usually cubes, can be collected almost everywhere—even in a salt shaker, in

which every grain under magnification appears as a cube. In the enormous salt mines of Galicia and Wieliczka in Poland, many crystal groups are found with some cubes ten to twelve inches on an edge. There is a magnificent group, standing three or four feet high, in the Vienna Natural History Museum, with glass-clear crystals of this size. Handsome crystal groups are coming from many places in the United States, one being the salt lake-bed deposits of Searles Lake on the San Bernardino desert in California.

Fluorite, calcium fluoride, also crystallizes well in many of its deposits. The quantities of very beautiful specimens that once came from the English lead mines of Weardale and Durham, and the mines at Alston Moor, Cleator Moor and elsewhere, are no longer being produced. So many were originally circulated, however, that it is still possible to obtain them from dealers. The perfection of their crystals and the wide range of color are difficult to match. To replace them, the mines near Rosiclare and Cave-in-Rock in southern Illinois are now injecting

Copper minerals in three widely different forms. FACING, FAR LEFT: *Dioptase, copper silicate, from Guchab, Africa.* LEFT: *Chalcopyrite, copper iron sulfide, from Pennsylvania.* ABOVE: *Malachite, copper carbonate, from Bisbee, Arizona.*

into private collections large quantities of excellent specimens in a range of colors from tan to purple to sky blue. They lack the clarity and the strong blue fluorescence of English fluorite specimens, but are still very attractive.

OXIDES: So many oxide minerals occur in attention-demanding specimens with excellent crystals that selection of a small group is difficult. Certainly among them would be the common iron oxide *hematite*. Well-crystallized examples of hematite are black, and so splendent as to appear polished. Sharp, curved crystals from Elba are often arranged in roughly parallel, stacked groups that may have a brilliant luster or peacock-colored tarnish. From Brazil and Switzerland come specimens, also brilliant, on which the flat crystal plates are precisely arranged in unfolded rosettes. Those from Brazil tend to be heavier and more masculine-looking, while those from Switzerland are delicate and feminine, perched lightly on sparkling crystals of quartz and feldspar. In recent years there has been a trickle of shiny, blocky crystal groups coming from Bahia, Brazil. And any listing of hematite classics would have to begin with the shiny, black, rounded "kidney ore" specimens from Cumberland, England.

A unique classic occurrence for the iron and manganese oxide, *franklinite*, should be mentioned even though specimens are seldom available. It is a rare mineral except at Franklin, New Jersey. There it has been found in well-formed, black octahedrons of various sizes, often embedded in white marble. The largest of these, measuring seven inches on the edge of the octahedron, is in the Smithsonian Institution.

CARBONATES: *Witherite* and *aragonite* are chosen to represent the classic carbonates because it is possible to acquire them now in excellent spec-

imens. In the past, the most famous examples of witherite were in white, hexagonal-looking, pyramid-shaped crystals from Northumberland, England. These are no longer available, except from old collections. Meanwhile, the fluorite mines of southern Illinois have produced many well-formed crystals of equal or larger size, up to three inches across. They are pale tan rather than white, and are flat on the ends rather than pointed, which gives them a more squat, but still attractive, appearance.

Aragonite is found in many places and in many forms. Perhaps the best of the currently recovered aragonite classics come from Sicily and Spain. Pieces from both these places are identical with the specimens that came into collections fifty or more years ago. The Sicilian crystals are white and brilliant, occurring as hexagonal-looking twins on yellow sulfur. Most of the Spanish crystals are the same kind of twins and are just as sharply developed and brilliant. They differ from the Sicilian in that they usually occur as isolated crystal twins, rather than in groups, and are reddish-lavender to brown in color.

SILICATES: Enough good *tourmaline* specimens have come in the past from Elba, Madagascar, Brazil, New York, Connecticut, and elsewhere to build an entire classic collection of this mineral alone. Even with the excellent supply, however, good tourmaline specimens have never been inexpensive. Almost all of the material cut into tourmaline gemstones comes nowadays from the state of Minas Gerais in Brazil. Often a crystal will escape cutting or survive because it is of less than cutting quality. As a result, some are always available for collections.

Other mineral-specimen tourmaline crystals, in soft tones and combinations of green and pink,

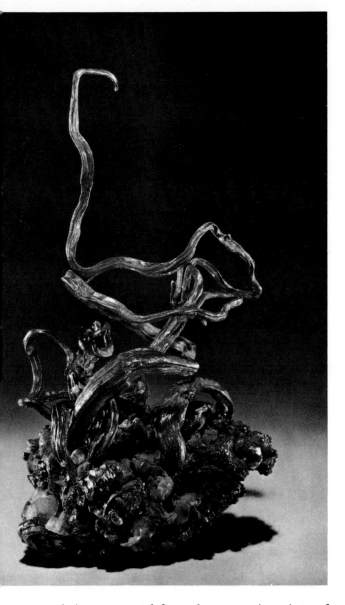

are being recovered from the pegmatite mines of San Diego County, California. Some of these are six inches or more in length and more than an inch in diameter, and some are completely developed on both ends.

From across our southern border, near Santa Cruz in Sonora, Mexico, black, lustrous, highly modified crystals of tourmaline are being found in the tungsten ore deposits. They so much resemble the shiny black crystals found years ago at Pierrepont, New York, that they are often confused with them. In the same deposits there are also strange groups of black tourmaline, looking

Shapely masses of entangled silver wires are typical
of the fine specimens of native silver from the rich ores
at Kongsberg, Norway. The fantastically twisted wires
are sometimes a foot long, and as thick as a man's wrist.

like tapered plumes, with deceptive velvety-looking surfaces.

Mexico is also producing specimens of *danburite*, another silicate, to replace the fine classic crystals that came at one time from the Toroku Mine on Kyushu, Japan. The Japanese crystals were single, well-developed shafts about four or five inches long, half to three-quarters of an inch thick, and usually opaque, though a few were transparent. Additional transparent, yellowish, rounded crystal masses suitable for gemstones were found in the gravels of Mogok, Burma. The newer specimens, coming out in a flood from Charcas in San Luis Potosí, Mexico, are far handsomer. They occur in groups of chisel-shaped crystals up to about four inches long. Although simple in form, they are bright, colorless to very pale pink, and transparent at the tips. Often they are in attractive groups jutting out like blades from the matrix material, and are sometimes associated with calcite crystals.

The list of classics, old and new, could be extended to include hundreds of others. The old *datolite* specimens from Westfield, Massachusetts, have given way to new ones from Prospect Park, New Jersey, and Loudon County, Virginia. Old *sphene* specimens from Switzerland are joined by excellent new specimens from Brazil. Famous *epidote* groups from Austria and Alaska are beginning to share honors with the new ones from Baja California. The shiny, black, *ilvaite* crystals from Idaho are even better than any recovered from Greece or Elba in the past.

If the connoisseur and collector now studying the old classics keeps an open mind, he soon finds that he is living in a time of the discovery of new mineral "Rembrandts." Any or all of the specimens merit inclusion in his collection.

The Science and Its Framework

7

Layer by layer, the earth sciences tell the story of the planet's past— and offer clues to the future

The ultimate goal of the science of mineralogy is to know as much as can be learned about mineral species and their relationships, both to each other and to the environments in which they form. Sometimes the knowledge can be put to immediate practical use but often, as is true in all sciences, it is sought for its own sake.

Mineralogy is one of a large number of working divisions of the earth sciences. It forms a bridge between geology on the one hand and chemistry and physics on the other. It is more closely related to geology than to chemistry and physics because it is concerned primarily with materials of the mineral kingdom. It is helpful, then, to understand the geological framework in which the science of mineralogy operates.

Geology is the study of the earth. Geological sciences include studies of rocks, ores, minerals, mineral fuels, fossils, and the natural processes from which they are all derived. These earth sciences, being broad in their coverage, rely heavily on other sciences. Chemistry, physics, mathematics, engineering, zoology, and botany are all involved in one way or another; their special contributions are vital in unraveling the story of the earth.

In recent years geology has expanded to take the planets under its wing. The United States Geological Survey is now preparing accurate maps of the moon and in several locations geological laboratories are being readied to study the first samples of minerals brought back from the moon.

THE GEOLOGICAL SCIENCES: The very broad spectrum of geological activities is reflected in the branches of the science that are generally recognized.

Geochemistry is the study of earth materials that seeks information about the chemical conditions that caused their occurrence, their movement in the earth, and their present distribution in the earth's crust. Increased understanding of nature's chemical processes also has high practical value in helping to predict the occurrence of ore deposits.

Geologic Mapping is a method of making an inventory of the contents and placement of various sections of the earth's crust for later research or economic exploitation. Photogeologic mapping is a specialized method of mapping based on the use of precisely located aerial photographs. The United States Geological Survey has already mapped about two-thirds of the United States, or 1,750,000 square miles, and is steadily increasing the total.

Geomorphology is concerned with the contours, forms, and details of the exposed parts of the solid earth and the natural processes that caused them. Lakes, mountains, valleys, plains, and beaches are in the province of the geomorphologist.

Geophysics is a complex branch of the science, comprising: seismology, a study of earthquakes and tremors; hydrology, a study of the occurrences and behavior of water in the crust of the earth; oceanography, a study of the oceans, their movements, currents, temperatures, composition, and the nature of ocean bottoms; terrestrial magnetism, a study of variations in the earth's magnetic field and the reasons for them.

Glaciology is the detailed study of present

PRECEDING PAGES: *A sample of olivine-rich dunite from North Carolina, ground to fraction of a millimeter thickness, is magnified five hundred times and photographed through a petrographic microscope.*

and long-past glacier activity. From it we derive information about the sequence of changes in earth temperatures, the characteristics of earth's oceans, and the effect of glacial periods on other geological processes and on life.

Historical Geology progresses toward the unraveling of the past history of the earth, based on evidence permanently preserved in rocks and fossils. Historical geology has been highly successful in reconstructing the geological story of the earth. The basic outline of the story is supported by sufficient evidence so as to be beyond doubt, although the details are constantly subject to modification as new evidence appears.

Micropaleontology is the study of microscopic fossils. The remains of very tiny animals called foraminifera, for example, have long been indicators of the ages and makeup of sedimentary rocks. This information can be especially useful for locating valuable petroleum deposits. There have even been attempts to set up a separate science of palinology, a study of fossil pollen.

Mineralogy, is the branch of geology that provides information on the classification, composition, internal structure, and chemical and physical behavior of minerals, the materials with which all of geology is ultimately concerned.

Paleobotany is fossil-plant study, in which the skills of geologist and botanist combine to analyze the occurrences and evolution of ancient plant types.

Paleontology, an all-inclusive science, gathers information concerning all plants and animals that have ever existed on the earth, and is invaluable to historical geology. Paleontologists maintain that "unless the remains of an animal still smell, they are the study material of paleontology." Scientists in this field often join the skills

Ferns, cycads, lepidodendrons, and other foliage, in an artist's conception of a prehistoric carboniferous forest. Coal was produced as thick layers of vegetation were broken down by time and pressure, leaving pure carbon.

and knowledge of biology with those of geology.

Petrography provides methods for the systematic description and classification of rocks. Petrography requires a thorough familiarity with mineralogy so that minerals can be recognized as they occur in rocks. Accurate rock descriptions are basic to any study of rock formation and change.

Petrology is the study of the natural history of rocks, their origins, present condition, alteration, and decay. The science relies heavily on mineralogy, but deals with the assemblages of minerals composing rocks rather than with individual minerals. These composite samples are much more revealing of processes within the earth than are the individual minerals.

Sedimentation is a specialized geological field, because the problems in understanding rock sediments are different from those posed by other kinds of rocks. The original rocks from which the sediments came usually leave little evidence of what they were before erosion tore them apart. A special procedure has been developed for the study of sedimentary rocks and the processes that formed them, to overcome the difficulties resulting from the fragmentation of the original material.

Stratigraphy uses evidence from several other branches of geology to describe the age, character, thickness, and sequence in which rock layers formed.

Structural Geology is the field of the geologist interested in the folding and breaking of rock layers, resulting in the deformation of the earth's crust. Studies of mountain building are typical of these researches.

THE MODERN GEOLOGIST: The United States is the largest consumer of minerals and mineral fuels in the world. These resources must be searched out and developed before they can be converted to practical use. An increasing number of highly specialized geologists supply the skills to do this. There are exploration geophysicists, petroleum geologists, economic geologists, groundwater geologists, engineering geologists, and even military geologists. More than two hundred colleges and universities in the United States now offer degrees of various kinds in the earth sciences.

It must already be obvious that the stereotype of a geologist as a grizzled prospector, wandering in the rocky wilderness with his burro and his rock hammer, dates back to the days of silent movies. A geologist may spend his entire career working in the field on various projects, but it is equally possible that he will choose to confine himself to full-time laboratory research work.

In the field the geologist, working with modern equipment, carefully measures and traces rock outcroppings to provide accurate observations from which geological maps can be made. These maps will eventually show details of hills, valleys, streams, and other surface features of the countryside. They may also show the nature of the underlying rock deposits that formed the surface features, give information as to their origin, or even indicate rock deposits for potential economic development. The geologist will also collect samples for later detailed laboratory study.

An office-bound geologist assembles and correlates information obtained through field parties and other kinds of research, and attempts to extract useful meaning from the information.

In the laboratory, the earth scientist carries out physical and chemical studies of the materials of the earth, assembling more information and testing various theories about their characteristics and origins.

There are a number of professional geological endeavors in which many earth scientists have been involved, each contributing his part. One of the most fascinating examples of such projects has involved hundreds of geologists from everywhere in the world for many years. They have slowly assembled, as in a jigsaw puzzle, the geological history of the earth.

FACING, TOP: *Fossil trilobite in shale, found near Lebanon, Pennsylvania.* BELOW: *Fossil ammonite from Dorset, England.*
TOP: *In 1833, an artist's conception of a prehistoric scene mixed flora and fauna from many geologic periods.*

171

Shortly after the Reformation, about the time other physical sciences were getting their start, Archbishop Ussher of Ireland made a name for himself by working out, from the Scriptures, a date for the creation of the earth. He set it at 9 A.M. on the morning of October 26, 4004 B.C. Probably because of his exalted position, the date was somehow entered as a footnote in the King James Bible.

For decades the true history of the development of the earth's features was obscured by the popular prejudice created by this reckoning. Since, according to the Archbishop, the existing features of the earth had been formed in only fifty-six hundred years, it was obvious that everything must have been done in a terrible hurry. All the gravels and unconsolidated sediments were thought to be remnants of Noah's great flood. Mountains were thought to have been thrown up in an instant, with great violence. Deep valleys were considered the result of clefts left by violent earthquakes that accompanied these rapid changes. There just had not been enough time, since the creation, for any other earth-shaping process.

One hundred thirty years later a Scottish geologist, James Hutton, made the first serious attack on these notions. In 1785 he advanced his Law of Uniformitarianism, which stated that the geological processes taking place now are the same ones that have always been taking place, and that the existing features of the earth were formed in the same way in which similar features are being formed today. If this could be substantiated (as it later was), it would indicate that the earth required enormous amounts of time to form its features. The earth, instead of being a few thousand years old, was a few billion years old. Every bit of geological, chemical, astronomical, and physical evidence now supports this thesis, but geological proofs were long and slow in coming.

The scientific study of the earth's actual age was given impetus with the development of two ideas. One, the self-evident Law of Superposition, holds that in any series of sedimentary rock layers the most recent sediments, or the younger rocks formed from the sediments, are on top, and the older at the bottom. The other, introduced by geologist William Smith in England in various rock layers, but it was obvious that each layer had its distinct fossil trademarks.

The evidence for both the Law of Superposition and the significance of index fossils is somewhat affected by the erratic behavior of the earth's crust. Some areas are so disturbed by the folding of rock layers that older rocks have been pushed up on top. In other places the layers are interrupted or duplicated by breaking and shifting motions.

Yet there remains overwhelming geological evidence to support these important ideas. Geologists, studying rock layers around the world, have been able to assemble the layers in a continuous series called the geologic column. Its contents record a sort of time chart of the sequence of geologic events that has transpired on the surface of the earth. No one part of the earth has a complete section of the column, but in spite of this it has been possible to piece together a series of layers that would be one hundred miles thick if piled all in one place.

After one hundred fifty years at the work of dating rock layers—or stratigraphy—geologists have become quite skilled at it. Following are some of the tests they have developed which, taken together, provide reliable information.

Lithologic similarity: When two beds of sedimentary rock are found, separated by considerable distance but made of identical rock materials, they are very likely parts of the same layer.

Continuous tracing: Any rock layer that can be traced continuously from one place to another through exposures and outcroppings is obviously the same age throughout.

Similar thickness: Rock layers in two different sequences may very well be of the same age if they are identical in thickness.

Similar positions: If two dissimilar layers of

before 1800, is the concept of index or guide fossils. Smith found that in any given rock layer only certain kinds of plant and/or animal fossils were preserved. He did not know why they differed

FACING, FAR LEFT: *Archbishop James Ussher arbitrarily dated the Creation at 4004 B. C.* LEFT: *Geologist James Hutton, chemist Dr. Joseph Black made eighteenth-century contributions to science.* ABOVE: *Early microscopes.*

rock in two localities occupy the same position in a sequence in which other layers are known to be identical, then they too are the same age.

Gradation over a distance: A single rock layer traced over a distance may be seen to blend into a different layer with considerable interpenetration at their edges. The two layers are the same age.

Identical fauna: Comparing the fossils in two widely separated rock layers will show whether or not they are at the same evolutionary stage. If they are, the rock layers are the same age.

Dissimilar fossils: Two rock layers in isolated places may contain different sets of fossils but still be the same age. If both sets of fossils occur elsewhere in one rock layer, then they are known to represent the same age. This means the original two rock layers are also the same age.

Using these guides, and developing the geologic column, a very detailed and lengthy history has slowly come to light. For convenience, the historical geologist divides this history into eras which begin and end with great crustal revolutions.

These revolutions interrupt the steady erosional and sedimentary pattern, which goes along undisturbed for millions of years between upheavals. The most recent revolution is the one that, through tremendous uplifts, gave birth to the Alps, the Himalayas, the Andes, the Sierra Nevadas, and other mountains. This revolution, with its predecessors, has divided into five parts the time during which there has been life on earth.

According to stratigraphic dating, first suggestions of fossil life appear in rocks over five hundred million years old. Traces of certain low plant forms called algae, and some primitive sponges, have been found in these rocks. Evolution continued, and in the *Paleozoic Era*, beginning five hundred million years ago, fish and some conifers—cone-bearing trees—began to develop. By two hundred million years ago, the dinosaurs had started developing in the *Mesozoic Era*. Toward its end, seventy million years ago, they went into decline. Mammals and flowering plants then made their ascent in the *Cenozoic Era*.

Man has put in his appearance among the mammals only in the last million years or so. The anthropologist D. J. Mahoney in a 1943 review of the antiquity of man, portrayed the development graphically when he said, "We may imagine ourselves walking down the avenue of time into the past and covering a thousand years at each pace. The first step takes us back to William the Conqueror, the second to the beginning of the Christian era, the third to Helen of Troy, the fourth to Abraham, and the seventh to the earliest traditional history of Babylon and Egypt. ... One hundred thirty paces take us to Heidelberg man, and about a quarter-mile to the oldest undoubted stone implements of Europe. And should we decide to continue our journey until we meet the

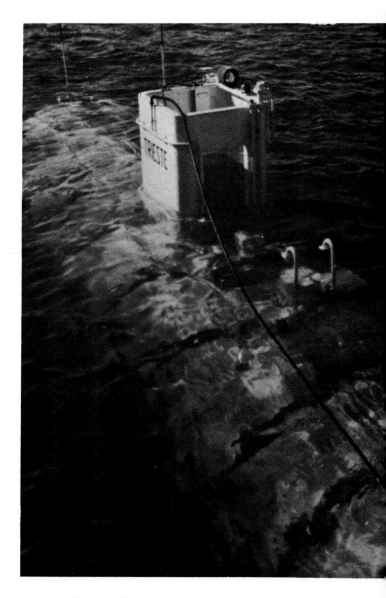

most ancient fossil organisms, the journey would exceed two hundred fifty miles."

The task of cooperatively filling in all the details of the journey is one of the greatest monuments the science of geology has erected to itself. In this work, the science of mineralogy makes constant and vital contributions.

MINERALOGY, THE SCIENCE: For convenience, the science of mineralogy has traditionally been divided into crystallography, physical mineralogy, chemical mineralogy, and descriptive mineralogy.

FACING: *Alexander the Great's diving boat was probably a legend, but man has always made efforts at undersea exploration.* ABOVE: *The Navy's submarine Trieste, and other advanced devices, now provide data never before available.*

A mineralogist's work may be in any or all of these divisions, particularly since they are arbitrary and may overlap considerably.

Crystallography had its beginnings in the measurement and study of relatively large and well-formed crystals. Now it has become a major science of basic importance in chemistry, physics, metallurgy, and biology.

Previously its major concern was with the external shapes and symmetries of crystals. These were accurately measured by the use of a narrow beam of light, reflecting from crystal faces. Now almost total interest has turned to their internal structures, as revealed by X-ray techniques. External symmetry is considered merely the necessary effect of internal structural causes.

Chemical mineralogy concerns itself with the elements of which minerals are made. Compositions and variations in composition are determined by traditional wet chemistry methods, using test tubes, chemical solutions, acids and so forth, or by electronic instruments. This information is later compared with information about the elements' structures to determine the effect they have on each other. Chemical mineralogy is also interested in the association of various species as they occur together in nature. This gives some indication of the chemical environment in which they grew. In turn, this reveals to the chemist the kinds of chemical activity that nature permits in mineral deposits, and how the natural activity compares with chemical reactions occurring in the laboratory.

Physical mineralogy is concerned with the physical characteristics of mineral species. Their behavior, hardness, tenacity, and other physical characteristics show a close relationship to their compositions and structures. Because many of the physical properties determined for minerals have proved to be significant in industry, they are coming under increasingly intensive study.

Descriptive mineralogy attempts to assemble enough information about each mineral species so that it can be sharply defined and not confused with any other. This usually means, in modern times, a chemical analysis to fix its composition, and a study of its crystals to determine their shape and symmetry, as well as X-ray analysis to find the symmetry of the structure and the size and shape of the unit cell. An optical analysis determines its refractive indices and other behavior toward light.

The scientific language used for describing and defining a mineral species is exceedingly abbreviated. Yet, when translated, mineralogical language conveys all the significant facts. A remarkable amount of time, energy, and sometimes complex equipment is involved in fashioning the description. As an example, we will translate and investigate the formation of an abbreviated description of the mineral species wurtzite. *Crystallography*—Hexagonal-P; dihexagonal pyramidal-6mm a : c = 1 : 1.6349.

This means that the mineral crystallizes in the hexagonal system; information is given about the mineral's symmetry; the ratio, a : c, explains that the vertical axis of a wurtzite crystal is 1.6349 times as long as any one of the three horizontal axes. The crystallography may be determined from measurement of well-formed crystals, or from X-ray examination. It is best if both methods can be used as a check on each other.

If crystals are measured, the instrument used is a two-circle goniometer. This instrument was perfected in the late 1800s in Austria by Professor Victor Goldschmidt and his mechanic, who gave his name—Stoe—to several fine old instruments that are still giving good service.

The crystal to be measured is mounted on the goniometer, which is ingeniously designed so that the crystal can be turned in any direction. A narrow beam of light, coming from a light tube, is bounced off one crystal face after another, into a telescope sight at the eye of the observer. The position of the crystal face is recorded from a reading of numbers marked on two movable circles on the instrument. Each set of numbers is then plotted as a kind of graph. From this graph, called a gnomonic projection, the symmetry of the crystal can be read. The graph can also be

FACING: *Stromboli, still an active volcano, erupts on August 30, 1842.* RIGHT: *At the Dinosaur National Monument in Utah, visitors may watch a working paleontological occurrence. Here, part of the bone bed is being exposed.*

177

used to make a drawing of the original crystal by converting its measurements according to standard drafting procedures.

Habit—Hemimorphic pyramidal $[50\bar{5}2]$ and $[10\bar{1}1]$. Short prismatic to tabular $[0001]$. Usually striated horizontally on $[10\bar{1}0]$ and $[10\bar{1}1]$. Often fibrous or columnar; as concentrically banded crusts.

This information attempts to describe the general appearance of all crystals of wurtzite ever seen. From the above, the crystals are pictured as being normally somewhat flat, with the two ends of the crystal having different sets of faces. Certain faces are described as being grooved or striated. The appearance of masses of the mineral is given so that it can be recognized when not in single, measurable crystals.

Structure cell—Space group C6mc a_o 3.811, c_o 6.234, $a_o : c_o = 1.6358$ contains Zn_2S_2.

This is structure cell data acquired by X-ray. It is perhaps the most tersely stated of all and yet the most significant information obtainable about the species. It describes the internal structure, detailing the kind of lattice and its symmetry. It gives, as well, the shape and size of the unit cell and the atoms that are contained in each unit cell. The structural arrangement is hexagonal (C6mc) which agrees with the crystals measured with the goniometer. The length of the vertical dimension of the unit cell is actually 6.234 angstroms (c_0 6.234) and the horizontal dimension is 3.811 angstroms (a_0 3.811). When these lengths are compared with each other, the vertical dimension comes out 1.6358 times as long as the horizontal. This com-

pares very well with the 1.6349 obtained from crystal measurement given before. When the chemical composition and density measurements are combined with the dimensions of the unit cell it is possible to calculate that there are two zinc atoms and two sulfur atoms in each unit cell (Zn_2S_2).

There are several kinds of X-ray instruments currently in use. The X-rays are usually produced by a glass-jacketed tube containing a filament and a water-cooled target.

In thousands of years, Monte Rosa Glacier in Switzerland will have ground a U-shaped bed out of its valley. Like all glaciers, Monte Rosa moves through partial melting, and on its way picks up and deposits material in moraines.

179

Forty to fifty thousand volts are applied to the tube, and electrons streaming from the filament are smashed into the target by this high voltage, causing it to produce X-rays. The kinds of X-rays produced depend on the kind of target in the tube. Usually a copper target is used, but for iron, cobalt, and manganese minerals these X-rays cause undesirable fluorescence. An iron target gives better results. The tube has two or four small circular windows, about half an inch in diameter, covered by very thin plates of beryllium metal or mica. These materials are quite transparent to X-rays, even though they may look opaque to the eye.

When the beam of X-rays is directed at a solid, much of it passes through the solid with no alteration, some of it is scattered, and some is converted to heat or other kinds of energy. It is the scattered X-rays that are of interest because they are the ones that have hit atoms on the way through. A picture of these scattered X-rays is taken by proper placement of a photographic plate. A large number of atoms all uniformly placed in the structure will scatter the X-rays in the same direction and reinforce their image on the film. The others are scattered in various directions and produce no combined mark on the film. This means that every different plane of atoms in the structure leaves its print on the film. By careful measurement of the film markings and suitable mathematical treatment of the measurements, the entire internal structure is revealed.

The X-ray method most often used is the powder diffraction procedure. The source of the X-rays is as described above, but the camera to hold the sample and film is unique. The camera is a flat, hollow metal cylinder, one end of which is a removable lid. It is very carefully machined to

exact dimensions, since its uniformity and the size of its diameter are crucial in the final film measurement. There is a hole on one curved side for the entrance of X-rays, and a hole opposite for the exit of most of them. Tapered metal tubes fit in these entrance and exit ports to guide the X-rays to and from the sample, which is mounted on a rotating spindle at the exact center of the camera. The film is a long, narrow strip that fits flat against the inside wall of the cylinder. It has two holes that fit over the entrance and exit port tubes.

In operation, the sample is mounted, the film is loaded in the darkroom, and the lid is replaced. As the sample spindle is turned by a motor-driven belt, the entrance port of the camera is placed against the X-ray source, and the exposure proceeds, taking several hours. When the film is developed, it has a series of matched curved lines running across it. These lines represent atomic planes; for each species their pattern is characteristic and will be different from that of any other species. The films can be indexed and filed and used in the same way as fingerprints.

More information, and more precise measurement with simpler mathematical treatment, can be obtained by using a precession-type camera, perfected by Dr. Martin Buerger of the Massachusetts Institute of Technology. It refines a method first used at the beginning of X-ray crystallography. Making measurements and calculations from these early films was difficult because there was a distortion of distances on the film. This distortion increased the farther the dots were from the center. Buerger overcame this difficulty with his precession camera, a mechanical contrivance that moves the film through strange gyrations during the exposure. Although exposures may run for two or three days, the resulting film is free from bothersome distortions.

Another apparatus often used in crystallography is the X-ray diffractometer. This instrument, performing the same function as the powder camera method, is more expensive than some of the others and requires a larger mineral sample. However, it gives very precise recordings of the spacings between planes of atoms, which are measured with some difficulty on the powder and precession camera films. It also gives the precise intensity for X-ray reflections from each plane. The sample is ground and smeared out with an adhesive on a glass slide. The slide is then placed in line between the X-ray tube and a Geiger counter. The counter moves in an arc about the sample as the X-rays come through it, picking up the reinforced X-rays that are scattered by the sample at different angles. The Geiger tube is con-

nected through electronic circuits to a recording device, which automatically draws a chart, showing peaks on the graph when reinforced X-rays scattered from a plane of atoms hit the counter. Since the chart is on a larger scale and more easily read than a film, the results are in a more practical form.

There are other X-ray devices in use, as well as several modifications of the devices described here; the X-ray crystallographer has available to him a good deal of special-purpose equipment. *Chemistry*—Zinc Sulfide, ZnS. Contains, in addition, some iron (8 percent maximum) and cadmium (3.66 percent maximum).

The description of the chemical composition of wurtzite shows that it is not a pure compound of zinc and sulfur but contains considerable iron and cadmium, as impurities or in substitution for some of the zinc atoms.

Despite new electronic devices now available in the mineralogical laboratory, the skilled analytical chemist is indispensable. His broad chemical knowledge and traditional "wet" techniques provide essential facts.

Chemical analysis of minerals was widely practiced for decades before anything was known about their structures. Naturally, the methods of chemistry have progressed along with the rest of the science. Many analytical chores are now performed by electronic equipment. But the other extreme is the simplest kind of chemical investigation: the spot test. In this kind of test the chemist is checking for a specific element or group of elements he thinks might be present in the sample. Taking a small part of the sample, he adds a few drops of an indicated chemical solution and watches to see if the expected results are produced. For example, when a drop of vinegar or hydrochloric acid is placed on a piece of calcite, it responds by giving off quantities of bubbles of carbon dioxide gas, proving that it is one of the carbonate family of minerals. Very precise spot tests, much more reliable and useful than this one, have been devised for many of the elements and their compounds.

But nothing can replace a complete, thorough, painstaking analysis by the chemist in his laboratory, where he has a wide array of glassware, chemical materials, weighing instruments, and other aids. As he goes carefully through his procedures, step by step, he discovers which elements are present in his sample, and in what quantities. His success depends on his knowledge of techniques, his judgment in deciding which techniques to use, and his skill in carrying them out.

Obviously, his task would be very much simplified, and considerable time and material would be saved, if the chemist knew which elements were present before he started. He could then determine the quantities of each element and be secure in ignoring the possible presence of others. In all modern laboratories this information can

be obtained by spectrographic methods, among others. The spectroscope is based on Isaac Newton's original discovery that a beam of light is split into various wavelengths as it passes through a glass prism. In actual practice a glass prism can be used in the instrument, but it is more usual to use a diffraction grating. The sample to be examined is powdered and placed between two carbon rods. A very high voltage arc is struck across the carbons and the sample is vaporized in the arc. As the atoms in the elements of the sample are heated in the arc they glow brightly to incandescence. The wavelengths of light given off by each kind of atom are different. The prism or diffraction grating sorts them out. After sorting, they fall on a photographic film and are recorded. By comparing the developed film with a standard measuring film, all the wavelengths can be identified; the elements that caused them to appear are known, as are the quantities of each.

One of the most complex chemical instruments to be devised in recent years is the extremely expensive electron microprobe. It can perform chemical analyses, impossible by wet methods, at a very high rate of speed. The sample to be analyzed can be less than one micron in diameter (three hundred-thousandths of an inch), too small to see without magnification. The sample is first prepared by grinding it flat, polishing its surface, and coating it with a very thin layer of graphite. Then the probe shoots a high-intensity, tightly focused beam of electrons through a vacuum at the sample, which is also in the vacuum chamber. The beam hits the target and excites the atoms into giving off their own particular kind of radiation. The radiation is collected and sorted by devices called curved crystal spectrometers. The sorted X-ray wavelengths are counted automat-

TOP: *Agate from Kambambi, Madagascar.*
LEFT: *Wavellite from Germany.*
ABOVE: *Iridescent fossil shell,*
South Dakota. The agate's bands,
the wavellite's needles, and
the fossil's iridescence are problems
for the physicist; chemical
analysis does not explain them.

183

ically and the information fed directly from the counters into computers. The information can be typed out by automatic typewriter as a set of numbers, or recorded in graph form by an automatic inking pen. If the beam is used to scan, like radar, across a larger sample, a picture will appear on a special oscilloscope tube, like a television tube, and can be photographed. If the scanning is set for a single element, iron for example, the photograph will show only those sample areas containing iron. No matter how the information is extracted, mathematical treatment of the results will give a good, serviceable chemical analysis in a short time.

Optical properties—Uniaxial positive. Indices O 2.356, E 2.378 for sodium light.

This information, obtained from the behavior of wurtzite with light, tells us that wurtzite is either hexagonal or tetragonal and that it has two different indices of refraction, 2.356 and 2.378, as expected for a doubly refracting substance. The light used to test the sample was from a sodium lamp, commonly used for this purpose because it has restricted wavelengths of light rather than the whole range of white-light wavelengths. Since the amount of refraction differs with different wavelengths of light, using only certain restricted wavelengths gives precise refraction measurements rather than a whole range of measurements for white light.

The petrographic or polarizing microscope was developed in the nineteenth century. Even with the advent of X-ray equipment, the polarizing microscope remains one of the most important basic tools for the mineralogist. Its importance is based on the fact that the effect of solids on light is a direct result of their structures. A knowledge of their optics, then, is an important key to a complete knowledge of the structures of minerals.

The polarizing microscope differs from ordinary microscopes in several ways. It does much more than merely magnify the specimen. Beneath the stage of the microscope, upon which the sample mineral sits, is a calcite crystal cut and polished in such a way that light coming through it, unlike normal light, vibrates in a single direction—or is polarized. Often a sheet of polaroid is used in place of the calcite crystal. The polarized light passes through a hole in the stage and up through the sample. Samples to be examined may be tiny mineral grains or "thin sections" of rocks. A thin section is prepared for this microscope from a small slab sawn off the rock and then ground so thin that light will come through it. An average thickness would be about thirty microns (not quite one-thousandth of an inch). Farther up the microscope tube is another calcite crystal just like the polarizer down below. The two crystal polarizers, called nicol prisms, are placed so that one passes light vibrating in one direction and the other passes light vibrating only at right angles to it. This means that without a sample in place the observer sees a black field through the tube. No light can pass. When isometric mineral samples or glass samples are placed on the stage between these crossed prisms, the field remains dark. Other mineral grains of other crystal systems, because of their light-refracting abilities, will be illuminated in the field.

The polarizing microscope is quite flexible. It can be used to determine the refractive index of a mineral, to reveal the presence of twinning in crystals, and to sort out minerals of different crystal systems. Grains that show no double refraction in any position are either glass or isometric minerals. Other grains that show no double

Back-scattered Elements

Sulfur

Iron

Magnesium

Calcium

Manganese

refraction in only one position are tetragonal or hexagonal. Still others that show no double refraction in two different directions are orthorhombic, monoclinic, or triclinic minerals.

Physical properties—Cleavage [11$\bar{2}$0] easy, [0001] difficult. H 3.5-4, G. 3.98, 4.1 [artif.], 4.1 [calc.]. Luster resinous. Color brownish black. Streak brown.

This gives additional general information about physical properties. From it we learn that wurtzite has a good cleavage in one direction and a weak cleavage in another. It tells us that the hardness is between 3.5 and 4—a fairly soft mineral. The specific gravity was measured on natural material to be 3.98, which compares quite well with measurements made on synthetic material at 4.1. In turn, the specific gravity of synthetic material is exactly what it should be, as predicted from X-ray information. Luster, color, and streak complete the description.

Any mineral having all the crystallographic, X-ray, chemical, and physical characteristics described here must be wurtzite and no other. The use of the instruments and techniques described, as well as many others, helps to insure the accuracy of the information.

As with any large group of professional people, there are a number of organizations catering to the interests and needs of geologists. The Geological Society of America is an all-inclusive grouping of professional geologists in this country. Other, more specialized, societies include the Geochemical Society, Paleontological Society, Society of Vertebrate Paleontologists, and the one that involves mineralogists per se, the Mineralogical Society of America.

The Mineralogical Society of America is composed of members working with materials that

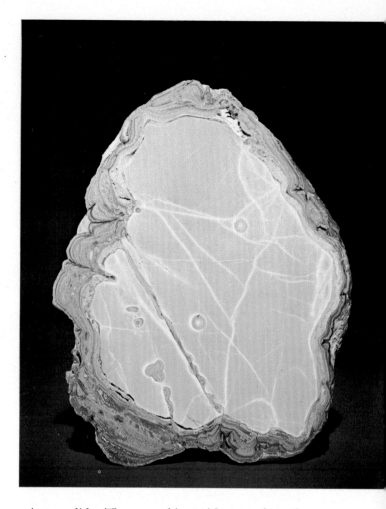

exist as solids. Those working with natural products are in the majority, but there are also many members who work with synthetic substances because the theories, laboratory techniques, and methods of study overlap. The Society was born at Harvard University on December 30, 1912, when twenty-eight professional mineralogists got together for the purpose. It has grown and prospered steadily since that time. From the small beginning, the Mineralogical Society of America membership has now grown to about twenty-five hundred. This still seems a small number, especially when compared to the many thousands of amateurs in clubs peripherally involved with mineralogy. In fact, it is an interesting sidelight that

FACING, TOP: *Millerite, a nickel sulfide in iron ore, from a defunct iron mine in Antwerp, New York.* LEFT: *From Griqualand, South Africa, a pseudomorph of quartz after crocidolite.* ABOVE: *An exceptional specimen of variscite.*

amateur clubs, like the New York Mineral Club and Philadelphia Mineral Society, had been organized much earlier. Nevertheless, the Society is the strongest, most active professional mineralogical group in the world.

In 1920 the Mineralogical Society of America took over sponsorship of a small magazine previously published by other groups, and the *American Mineralogist* began to prosper. In 1926 it was endowed handsomely by Washington A. Roebling, an amateur interested in mineralogical affairs. Later grants of money came from the Geological Society of America. Today the publication is internationally significant, with over two-fifths of the published copies going to subscribers abroad. It averages more than fifteen hundred pages a year and its contents are of high scientific quality.

In addition to the *American Mineralogist*, the Society is engaged, jointly with the Mineralogical Society of Great Britain, in publication of *Mineralogical Abstracts*. This is a periodical that gives very short reviews, or abstracts, of all scientific papers of concern to mineralogists that are being published in all the world's journals. The abstracts keep the practicing mineralogist informed of developments in his own science.

Each year, in conjunction with the general meetings of the Geological Society of America, there is a meeting of the Mineralogical Society. Scientific papers are read and discussed, and information and views are exchanged informally among professionals vitally interested in a common field of work. Usually a few guided field trips are offered as a firsthand educational experience. At these meetings, also, the Society makes its two coveted professional awards. One, the Roebling Medal, is considered the greatest honor a professional mineralogist can receive. It was established in 1937 in remembrance of Washington Roebling, and was awarded for the first time to Dr. Charles Palache of Harvard University. It is given for outstanding professional achievement in mineralogy and petrology. A more recent honor, the Mineralogical Society of America Award, has been awarded about fifteen times, five times to citizens of Great Britain. The recipient is honored for an outstanding contribution to the science made before he is thirty-five years old. The purpose, of course, is to recognize and encourage exceptional ability among younger members of the profession of mineralogy.

FACING, TOP: *X-ray powder-technique camera films atom patterns of powdered, rolled samples.* LEFT: *Similar but more precise data is given by X-ray diffractometer.* ABOVE: *A sample is placed in a spectroscope for arcing.*

Minerals at Work
8

*Today, minerals and their
products underlie an ever-more-
complex industrial civilization*

Space rockets, capsules and the hardware to launch them, supersonic jet airliners, nuclear power generators, and a host of other complicated fabrications have in recent years had a drastic impact on our exploitation of the mineral kingdom. The demand for rare metals, some previously known only as laboratory curiosities, has accelerated. New kinds of metal alloys, new kinds of crystals, and other substances with peculiar and unique properties are constantly being sought to satisfy the needs of an imaginative and rapidly expanding industrial technology. Most of these materials are extracted directly from the mineral deposits of the world or are manufactured from mineral products.

Everything man now uses except food, other agricultural products, and clothing, has been mined from the earth. Considering that all this mining underpins our industrial culture, it is amazing how little general interest or knowledge there is about it. Such matters are considered too technical and the proper business only of scientists, engineers, and technicians. Except in time of crisis, most governments show little interest in mineral exploration and study. Consequently, the exploitation of the world's mineral resources is left to drift, buffeted by political whim and the fluctuations of the market. Nevertheless, our industrial civilization and its advancement depends completely on mining and the practical use of the products of the mineral kingdom. The story of

the search for minerals, their extraction from the earth, and their application in industry is a fascinating one.

IRON: Homer mentions iron throughout the *Iliad*, his epic of the Trojan wars. For example, he tells of Achilles offering an iron quoit as a prize at the funeral of Patroclus. The ancient Greeks knew the metal, then, and considered it rare and precious. Iron objects have been recovered from Egyptian tombs dating from 3500 B.C. and earlier. By the time of the Hittites in Asia Minor, it was being worked in sufficient quantity for practical use. In 600 B.C., according to Byron's "Destruction of Sennacherib":

*The Assyrian came down like a wolf on the fold,
And his cohorts were gleaming in purple and gold;
And the sheen of their spears was like stars on
the sea . . .*

It is certain that those brightly shining spears were made of iron; these warriors were completely outfitted with iron armor and weapons.

It is safe to say, then, that mankind has had a practical technology for ironworking for at least three thousand years. During that period the use of iron, replacing stone and bronze, caused such drastic changes in man's life and activities that it has become known as the Iron Age. We are, perhaps, still in this age.

There is enough iron in the crust of the earth to account for most of the yellow, red, brown, and green colors seen in exposed soil and rocks. The amount of aluminum in the earth exceeds that of iron, but aluminum is more difficult to extract from its ores. Iron, therefore, is the commonest commercial metal.

The United States now has a production of iron

PRECEDING PAGES: *Minerals are used in new ways to meet the intricate
new demands of space technology. Light-sensitive plates of silicon,
which convert sunlight to electricity, coat a satellite in flashing blue.*

and steel of various compositions and purities—produced by several different processes—exceeding one hundred million tons a year. Of this amount about one-fifth is consumed by the automobile industry and the rest by railroads, construction, and the manufacture of machinery. In such quantity the costs of production are spread out and reduced; certain kinds of raw iron products now cost as little as one cent per pound.

To produce these prodigious quantities of iron and steel requires literally mountains of ore. The problem would be much simplified if iron were the only raw material needed. But to charge one of the enormous fiery blast furnaces that melt the iron from its ores usually requires three other important raw materials. For every four tons of iron ore smelted in the furnace, it is necessary to add about one ton of limestone to remove the silicate mineral impurities, two tons of coke to supply the heat and to keep the right amount of carbon in the mixture, and nine tons of air to keep the chemical reaction going. The air is free, but the coke must be made from coal and the limestone must be mined. The iron ores themselves must be mined. Through the years the United States has relied heavily on its own vast deposits. Now, however, as our supplies of higher-grade ores are badly reduced, we are importing more and more iron ore from abroad, most of it from Canada and South America.

There are three major ores of iron: magnetite, hematite, and limonite. Hematite is most commonly used because of its more general availability, purity, and high iron content. Hematite, the red ore of iron, is an iron oxide (Fe_2O_3) and theoretically contains as much as 70 percent iron. As

From the time of the Hittites, iron was used for armor and the tools of war. In a Renaissance concept of a classic myth, Giulio Romano painted Achilles receiving from Thetis the metal arms forged by Vulcan.

193

it is usually found in its deposits mixed with impurities, the percentage actually is lower, and deposits containing as little as 25 percent can be worked with profit. The most common impurities are quartz, clay, limestone, and traces of the elements manganese, titanium, sulfur, arsenic, and phosphorus. The presence of titanium and manganese can enhance the value of the ore, but sulfur, arsenic, and phosphorus are undesirable in the finished product.

In the district around Lake Superior lie the richest and most productive hematite mines in the world. The largest of these are the iron ranges in Minnesota, but there are others of the same type in nearby Michigan. Unfortunately, the best of these deposits were stripped off during World War II, and current operations are plagued with lower-grade ores containing excessive quartz. Processes have now been developed, however, to make mining and smelting of these high-silica taconites profitable.

There is considerable professional debate over the sources of these deposits. Some geologists consider them simple sedimentary beds. Others believe evidence proves that the iron and silica were carried upward by magmatic water and deposited on the floor of an ancient sea. Much of the silica then was leached, or dissolved away, converting low-grade deposits to usable ore.

Major Russian hematite deposits are located near Krivoi Rog in the Ukraine. Other new and important deposits have been found elsewhere, such as one on the Quebec-Labrador border in Canada, containing an estimated six hundred million tons of high-grade ore.

Black iron ore—magnetic ore—is less plentiful. It consists of the mineral species magnetite, which is also an oxide of iron (Fe_3O_4) and theoretically

may contain up to 72 percent iron. There are workable deposits of magnetite in the United States and in Russia, but the largest and best known are at Kiruna and Gellivare in northern Sweden. Swedish steel, made from ore mined at these deposits, has long had an excellent reputation. The mines are very large, open quarries and the deposits contain reserves estimated at one billion tons.

The common, yellow-brown bog-iron ore, or limonite, is of sedimentary origin and lower grade, with a maximum theoretical content of 60 percent iron. Limonite is a mixture of iron oxides with varying amounts of water in their compositions. It is often very impure because it is mixed with other sedimentary materials such as clay, sand, and gravel. The best-known and most productive

FACING: *Metallurgy in ancient China.* TOP: *Iron being smelted. The ore was puddled (at left) to purify it.* FAR LEFT: *Smelting tin.* LEFT: *Mercury smelted out of cinnabar.* ABOVE: *A Bessemer furnace in 1856; the process is basically the same today.*

for only about 5 percent of the steel made in the United States. The rest is made by the open hearth method. Between fifteen and twenty tons of liquid pig iron can be handled at one time in the egg-shaped Bessemer converter, while the open hearth method can handle between fifty and two hundred tons in each batch and is easier to control because the process takes much longer.

Smaller batches of special steels are made in electric furnaces, where they are heated for the addition of certain desirable elements such as nickel, cobalt, molybdenum, and vanadium. These give steels greater elasticity, greater hardness, high corrosion resistance, magnetism, and other desirable qualities.

ALUMINUM: Six times more iron in its various forms is produced in the United States each year than its nearest metallic competitor, aluminum. The competition has been keen, and aluminum has reached its prominent position in the metals market in less than eighty years. There are many uses for iron in which aluminum cannot be substituted, but many new applications have been developed for this common metal.

Since aluminum is much more plentiful in nature than iron, it is surprising to discover that it was unknown to the ancients. It was not until 1825 that the Danish chemist, Hans Christian Oersted, found a way to extract aluminum from its ores. Even then it was not possible to prepare it in quantity until 1850. At that time, although still difficult to prepare, it could be bought in small quantities at about the same price as gold. By the time the Washington Monument was built in 1884 the price was about five dollars a pound— low enough so that the monument could have an aluminum cap. The cap is still there crowning the sharply pointed top; if necessary, it could be

limonite mines are located in the Alsace-Lorraine district of France, and produce ore suitable for smelting.

All iron, which is smelted in great blast furnaces, is run off as a molten liquid to be cast in bars or pigs. From these it will eventually be converted into cast iron, wrought iron, or some kind of steel.

To make cast iron, the pigs are remelted and poured into molds to produce the proper shapes. Because cast iron resists heat, it can be used for stoves and fireplace grates. Since it does not rust easily, it is widely used for water pipes and gutters. It also is frequently used for large, basic parts of heavy machinery.

Wrought iron is low in carbon and is heated and worked or drawn while hot. This process makes it very tough and resistant to shock, unlike cast iron, which is brittle. Because of its toughness, wrought iron can be worked into chains, bolts, nails, pipes, and hinges, which are subject to abuse.

There are two methods for converting pig iron to steel. Of these, the Bessemer process accounts

ABOVE: *British coinage, 1842. The word coin derives from the wedge-shaped die—*cuneus*—that stamped out the metals.*
FACING: *Sixteenth-century decorative pewter plate; the tin-lead alloy was commonly used for utilitarian objects.*

replaced today with aluminum for only a few cents a pound.

In the year 1886 Charles Martin Hall found a way to separate aluminum away from its ores. The best ores of aluminum are those in which it is combined with oxygen with very strong chemical affinity. Bauxite, the best and commonest ore, is such an oxide with a small amount of water in its composition.

Hall's method made it possible to separate the tightly bound aluminum on a large scale and at a low enough cost to make the metal economically competitive. He discovered that aluminum oxide (Al_2O_3) would dissolve in melted cryolite (Na_3AlF_6). Cryolite is a mineral species that has been mined in commercial quantities at Ivigtut in Western Greenland. It melts at rather low temperatures, and is excellent for the purpose.

In Hall's process, the aluminum oxide is dissolved in melted cryolite in a carbon-lined container, and carbon bars are inserted into it. An electric current is run through the solution between the carbon bars and the carbon lining. The electric current drags the aluminum atoms away from the oxygen atoms. It settles as molten metal on the bottom of the container, where it can be tapped off as it accumulates. By the steady addition of aluminum oxide, the process can be kept going continuously until the carbon pieces need replacement. Of course, the process consumes fantastic amounts of electricity. Aluminum manufacture is therefore one of the major consumers of electricity in industry today.

The trouble with the early aluminum produced was that the metal lacked strength, was soft and extremely brittle, and had a tendency to flake and corrode. Metallurgists have found ways to increase its purity and to alloy or mix it with other metals for strength. As a result, aluminum can now be made as strong as steel, highly resistant to cor-

rosion, and is even available in several colors. Duraluminum is a good example of its alloys. It consists of 4 percent copper, 1 percent manganese, 1 percent magnesium, and the rest aluminum, and although not quite as strong as steel, is a satisfactory substitute, particularly because it has only one-third the weight of steel.

Because aluminum is lightweight and an excellent conductor of electricity, it is used for long-distance electrical transmission wires. Ordinary copper wires are quite heavy. Aluminum makes it possible to have larger wires that carry more current, without causing a weight-supporting problem.

Like iron, aluminum does corrode. However, there is a major difference. As the oxygen of the air attacks and combines with the exposed aluminum surface, it is held tightly by the strength of the attraction between them. This quickly coats the surface with a very thin, very tight-packed, transparent layer of aluminum oxide. Since no more oxygen can get through this protective layer to attack the fresh aluminum underneath it, corrosion stops. This layer of aluminum oxide also protects aluminum from the chemical attack of foods. Since it also conducts heat well it is ideal for cooking utensils.

GOLD: Among the Egyptians and other cultures in the cradle of western civilization gold was used at least as far back as 4000 B.C. It is used today as the basis of the world's money system, for ornamentation, and for jewelry. For centuries, then, it has had a high intrinsic value.

Gold is very well qualified to be a coinage metal. It is highly resistant to corrosion and chemical destruction of almost any kind. Also, it is soft and easily worked. Scarcity helps to keep its value high, but enough can be found to satisfy monetary or industrial needs. Silver, the only other true coinage metal, is more common and does not have the same degree of durability as gold; it takes a second position. All coins made of other metals are merely money tokens based on the value of stored gold and silver. Since it is illegal, for good monetary reasons, to circulate actual gold coins in the United States, our supply is secure in well-guarded vaults at Fort Knox.

There is an old joke that asks "which weighs more, a pound of gold or a pound of feathers?" It is not so much of a joke after all because two weighing systems are used in the United States. The troy system, with twelve ounces to the pound, is traditionally used for precious metals and for apothecary purposes. The avoirdupois system, with sixteen ounces to the pound, is used in general commerce. Gold, then, is traditionally figured at twelve ounces to the pound and feathers at sixteen ounces to the pound. Obviously a pound of feathers weighs more. However, gold is a heavy substance. A piece of it is three times as heavy as a piece of steel the same size. A small block of solid gold the size of a normal pack of cigarettes would weigh almost four and one-third pounds.

Gold is chemically inactive. Evidence of this is its occurrence in nature as a free metal, un-

FACING, FAR LEFT: *Thousands of formulas exist for making glass; quartz sand is basic to all.* LEFT: *Charles M. Hall invented the electrolytic production of aluminum.* RIGHT: *Extracted aluminum is poured into ceramic molds for casting.*

combined with other elements. Even in the laboratory, gold is not attacked by the common acids. The ancients found that a mixture of hydrochloric acid and nitric acid would dissolve it, though with some difficulty. They named this mixture *aqua regia*—royal water—since it could dissolve gold, king of metals. Although gold is so chemically inert that it cannot possibly corrode, it is a very soft metal and is usually alloyed with copper, silver, or nickel to make it hard enough for normal uses. Besides being soft, it is malleable, which means it can be easily beaten into sheets or drawn into wire. One ounce of gold can be beaten thin enough to make sheets that will cover an area thirteen feet square. One-third of a million sheets of this gold leaf would make a pile only about an inch high. Since gold can also be drawn into wires as thin as one two-thousandths of an inch in diameter, and has very high electrical conductivity, it finds critical uses in the electronics industry.

Sometimes the alloys of gold are more useful than the pure metal. This is especially so in coinage, ornaments, and other objects that suffer rough use. When absolutely pure, gold is labeled, for historical rather than scientific reasons, 24-karat gold. Most jewelry gold is alloyed with copper to give it strength and hardness. Quality jewelry is of fourteen parts of gold to ten of copper (14 karat) or eighteen of gold to six of copper (18 karat). Inexpensive jewelry that turns green or black after exposure to the weather or human skin contains too much copper and too little gold. Coinage gold in the United States contains 90 percent gold and 10 percent copper. Dental gold varies a bit but contains from 65 to 90 percent gold and 5 to 12 percent silver. Gold is also graded as to its "fineness," based on how

many parts out of one thousand are gold. An alloy of 85 percent gold and 15 percent copper would be 850 fine.

To extract gold from its crushed and roasted ores, the mercury amalgam method described in Chapter 4 is commonly used. Surprisingly, however, 25 percent of the gold mined in the United States comes from placer mining. The gold-bearing gravels so mined have come from the weathering and breaking-up into gravel deposits of the original gold-bearing mother lodes or veins. Because gold is so heavy, it tends to settle out and concentrate itself at the bottom of these deposits, so that a small tonnage of gravel concentrates can yield a high percentage of gold. Sometimes the gold nuggets in placer deposits are startlingly large. Historical reference is always being made to the "Welcome Stranger" nugget found at Ballarat, Australia, in 1886. It weighed a glorious 2280 ounces.

South Africa is currently the world's foremost producer of gold. Some of the richest mines occur in the Rand district around Johannesburg. Rich as they are, the Rand ores contain grains of gold too small to be seen by the naked eye. To the delight of the owners and operators, they also produce quantities of uranium.

The most favorable place to find gold, other than in placer deposits, is within a mile or so of a granite intrusion. The gold will have been deposited there by hydrothermal action. Some of the remarkable deposits at places such as Cripple Creek, Colorado, and Goldfield, Nevada, resulted from low-temperature hydrothermal action near the surface. This kind of vein is spectacular and fantastically rich, but such deposits are short-lived and do not persist at depth.

QUARTZ: This very common mineral has been

Most steel is produced by the open-hearth process,
easier to control than the Bessemer. In a steel mill at
Hamilton, Ontario, slag, which contains the dissolved
impurities, is poured from a typical open-hearth furnace.

put to many uses—some of them rather surprising. Quartz is found in nature as grains or masses that are white, gray, or sometimes highly colored. It also occurs in clear glassy crystals and masses that can be of considerable size. The largest single crystal on record was found near Itapore in Goiaz, Brazil. It was twenty feet long, and its estimated weight was over forty-four tons.

Much of the sand of ocean beaches is composed of quartz grains. Quartz in the form of sand has valuable direct use in the building trades when it is mixed in mortar and cement. In powder form, it is mixed in paints to give them heavier body; it is used in scouring soaps and on sandpaper to produce scratching or abrasion. It will eventually wear away most substances, though this does not apply to extremely hard metals or minerals.

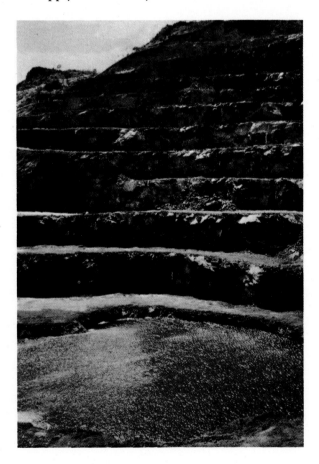

The glass industry also consumes large quantities of quartz in the form of sand. There are perhaps as many as fifty thousand different formulas for making glass, each one giving a product with slightly different characteristics. Typical of these is a simple soda-lime glass made by fusing together pure quartz sand with sodium carbonate and calcium carbonate. Bottle glass is a simple glass of this type, with a greenish color arising from traces of iron impurities. There is also a quartz glass made from pure sand alone—very expensive because it is difficult to prepare. A mixed-composition glass will melt, and can be worked, somewhere between 600 to 900 degrees Fahrenheit. Fused quartz glass, however, melts at 1500 degrees, and must be kept at that temperature while it is being worked. However, it has many advantages over other kinds of glass. It is transparent to ultraviolet light, which is stopped by ordinary glass. Sun lamps, and other lamps used as sources of ultraviolet light, must have bulbs made of quartz glass.

Fused quartz glass also withstands rapid changes in temperature without breaking. This characteristic is called a "low coefficient of expansion," meaning that there is very little expansion or contraction with changing temperatures. Even when the glass is unevenly heated or cooled, so that one part is hotter than another, there are practically no expansion stresses. Consequently, quartz glass is used extensively in the laboratory in the form of tubes, rods, and containers.

In one unusual process, melted quartz is forced out through a stream of high-pressure hot air. This spins the quartz out into a fluffy mass of fine fibers, from which a quartz paper is manufactured. This fiber, mixed with clay, is run through a paper-making machine to become quartz paper—

LEFT: *The exhausted west pit of an Australian uranium mine, Kathleen Uranium Limited.* FACING: *One of the end products: the mushroom-shaped trademark of the twentieth century—the cloud of an atomic explosion.*

a good electrical insulator because it will not conduct a current, nor will it break down when placed in a strong electrical field. At the same time it can withstand temperatures up to 3000 degrees Fahrenheit.

Quartz also has some interesting electrical characteristics. It is a piezoelectric mineral, meaning that crystals of quartz, when squeezed, develop electrical charges on certain surfaces. The process also works in reverse. If an electrical charge is applied to a crystal, internal stresses develop and it changes shape.

When free of bubbles, cracks, or flaws, and free of twinning in its internal structure, quartz is often used for piezoelectric devices. A disk or rectangular plate, cut from the quartz in very exact directions with carefully controlled dimen-

sions, is mounted between two electrical contacts and placed in a protective tube. This so-called oscillator is then introduced into an electronic device such as a telephone circuit or a radio apparatus—circuits that have an electric current pulsing through them alternately back and forth thousands or even millions of times per second. As this alternating current hits the quartz plate, the plate expands and contracts rapidly. Its dimensions have been chosen so that it vibrates—oscillates—at the same rate as the circuit current. The current and the quartz crystal plate must operate in unison so that, with the plate unable to change its dimensions, it keeps the circuit from alternating at anything other than a fixed rate. The device then becomes known as a frequency-control oscillator. It is responsible for the fact that every time you tune in your favorite radio station it is at the same place on the dial.

With the tremendous advances made in electronic equipment during World War II, quartz oscillator plates were critically needed. Since very little quartz of the proper kind exists in the United States, most of our supply came from Brazil. A good part of this electronic quartz is now grown here synthetically, but large amounts are still imported.

URANIUM: In 1789, uranium was discovered by the chemist Martin Klaproth in black pitchblende from the Czechoslovakian mines at Jachymov. He named the element after the planet Uranus, which had recently been discovered. Originally the Jachymov mines had been operated for their silver ores, which eventually ran low. They were then converted to lead mining, but little thought was given to the pitchblende they contained.

It was in this same black material that Becquerel discovered radioactivity in 1896, and Marja and Pierre Curie discovered polonium and radium in 1898. Even though by then acutely interesting to science, uranium and its ores were still commercially unimportant.

In 1939 the entire picture changed with the discovery of atomic fission. O. F. Hahn of Germany, repeating some of the atomic research of Enrico Fermi of Italy, reported certain unexplained results. These were correctly interpreted in 1939 by Lise Meitner and O. R. Frisch, who had fled from Nazi Germany and were working at the laboratory of Niels Bohr in Denmark. They were farsighted enough to recognize in atomic fission a phenomenon that would instantaneously release very large amounts of energy. Atomic fission is the splitting of the cores of certain kinds of atoms by bombarding them with other kinds

of atomic particles called neutrons. These cores, or nuclei, form atoms of lighter elements as they split, and in the process release tremendous amounts of raw energy.

Uranium atoms are not all the same. They come in different weights. The scientist tags them as uranium 235, uranium 238, and uranium 239. The one that undergoes fission is uranium 235. Unfortunately, only one part in one hundred forty of natural uranium is this kind.

Because all uranium atoms behave the same way chemically, there is no way to separate them by simple chemical sorting. Multimillion-dollar factories and whole cities like Los Alamos had to be created to handle the complex processes for sorting out the uranium 235. Along the way a method was found for creating a new element, plutonium, from the uranium raw materials. Plutonium has the same fission characteristics as uranium 235, but to a greater degree. Further, being a different element, plutonium has different chemical characteristics, and can be chemically separated from uranium.

Surmounting the difficulties of handling and processing tonnages of these rare and highly radioactive metals was an unbelievable chore for science and industry. But it was done, with results that, in 1945, wiped out Hiroshima and riveted the attention of the world.

Before 1923, the United States' deposits of carnotite, the yellow uranium vanadate mineral found on the Colorado Plateau, were the most important in the world. By 1929, however, rich deposits of mixed uranium minerals in the Belgian Congo had forced American producers from the market. Very soon afterward the world supply was heavily increased by deposits from Great Bear Lake, Canada. With the rapid change brought

204

FACING, TOP: *Orpiment, an arsenic sulfide, in rare crystals from Takab, Afschar, Iran.*
RIGHT: *Cinnabar, a mercury sulfide, in unusually large, dark red, twinned crystals from Hunan Province, China.*

about by the uranium fission discovery, however, there were more than one thousand operating mines in the United States by 1961. As the years wore on, uranium was overproduced, and production was cut back sharply at great financial loss. Currently, with the rapid development of nuclear power plants, the demand for raw materials has again increased.

RUBY: Much of the best natural ruby—a chromium-bearing variety of the mineral species corundum—is converted to gemstones. Off-colored or flawed ruby is sometimes used for bearings in watches and other delicate instruments. It is excellent for bearings because corundum, being so very hard, will not be worn away by the constant motion of a gear or wheel and needs no lubrication, as would a metal gear turning in a metal socket.

Because it is so easy to manufacture ruby these days (see Chapter 3), most of the highly technical uses for it are based on synthetic material. However, the raw material for making ruby still must be mined and purified. The ore of this aluminum oxide (Al_2O_3), or alumina, is bauxite, and is the same ore from which aluminum metal is extracted. Man-made ruby is prepared for bearing manufacturers in long, thin, cylindrical rods of the required diameter for the finished bearing. These rods are sliced into little circular tablets of the desired thickness.

The impurities that cause red coloring in corundum have no importance in bearings, but they have a most significant effect on the electronic characteristics of the mineral. They are responsible for the most fantastic new use to which any mineral material is being put—the application of synthetic ruby in masers and lasers. The two words are rapidly becoming part of everyday vocabulary, even though what they describe is largely a mys-

tery to the public. Maser is an abbreviation for "microwave amplification through stimulated emission of radiation." The device, often built around a synthetic ruby rod, can receive a weak radio signal and be stimulated by it into giving off its own radio signal of the same wavelength—but one thousand times more powerful. Such devices are of enormous importance in receiving weak television and radio signals bounced off communications satellites, like Telstar, and amplifying them for rebroadcast. They also receive and amplify the very faint radio signals that radio telescopes receive from distant stars and galaxies, thus helping us to extend our knowledge of the heavens.

An optical maser is very similar to a radio- and television-type maser, except that it deals with light. It is called a laser—an abbreviation of "light amplification through stimulated emission of radiation." Ruby rods for lasers have a long, slender, cylindrical core of ruby that is covered by an overlying sheath of sapphire. Around the laser rod is placed a coil-shaped, brilliant xenon arc lamp. When it flashes, the light from this lamp enters the rod through the sapphire coat. Because sapphire is such a good refractor and reflector, it traps the light inside the rod. This brilliant light excites the chromium atoms in the ruby into giving off their own continuous, high-intensity, coherent light beam. (A "coherent" light beam is one that is very narrowly and tightly focused and is all of one wavelength vibrating in unison, in contrast to white light with its haphazard mixture of wavelengths.)

This beam of light, as it shoots out the end

of the laser rod, is so narrow and so intense that it can be transmitted over enormous distances without being lost. A beam of red laser light vibrates nearly a billion times as fast as ordinary radio waves. Radio waves are modulated, or modified, by radio transmitters to carry messages. It is theoretically possible also to modulate a laser beam for carrying messages. Because of its great vibration rate the laser beam could carry far greater quantities of information than do radio waves. And there is now a new technique for modifying the laser beam, using a powerful magnetic field that increases its power one thousand times more!

In addition to communication, the concentrated light power of lasers will probably one day help us to destroy missiles, bore holes in steel, make three-dimensional photographs, navigate satellites, and fight cancer. It is already being explored as a new surgical technique.

SULFUR: The most important single chemical substance used in a modern industrial country is sulfuric acid. In one way or another, it is involved in nearly every industrial process. Sulfuric acid is made from the element sulfur, along with air and water. In the United States, our tremendous sulfur deposits are found in the rocks lying on top of great intrusive plugs of rock salt called salt domes. Such a dome may have in its capping tens of millions of tons of sulfur.

These salt domes, located in Texas and Louisiana, pose a difficult mining problem. The deposits lie at considerable depth under quicksand and other rock layers. In 1894 a Philadelphia-trained chemist named Herman Frasch devised an ingenious method of recovering this deeply buried material. Three concentric pipes are forced from the surface down into the area of the deposit.

FACING, TOP: *Traffic-light glass is produced with mineral coloring agents.* BELOW: *Natural ruby, not as good for industrial use as larger, purer, laboratory-grown stones.* ABOVE: *Yttrium garnet made at Bell Telephone laboratories.*

The outer pipe carries down superheated water at about 360 degrees Fahrenheit. Compressed air, at 400 pounds per square inch, is carried down the innermost pipe. When the hot water reaches the deposit, it melts the sulfur, which is then forced up through the middle pipe by the compressed air. Since this middle pipe is surrounded by the hot water pipe, the sulfur remains hot and molten all the way up. At the surface, the sulfur, water, and compressed air mixture froths out into towering rectangular vats, where it is allowed to settle, cool, and harden. The sides of the vats are later removed, and the rectangular mountains of sulfur are mined with bulldozers, power shovels, and other heavy equipment. About 60 percent of the United States' supply of sulfur is obtained this way.

The other major source of sulfur is the iron and sulfur mineral pyrite, which is mined like most other solid ores. When the pyrite is roasted, some of its sulfur combines with air to form sulfur dioxide (SO_2), which is then used to make sulfuric acid. Enormous deposits of pyrite are found in Spain in an area extending from the province of Seville westward to Portugal. The ores in this belt very likely represent a good half of the world's sulfur reserves.

GARNET: With sharper edges and greater hardness than quartz, garnet is especially valuable in the woodworking industry as garnet paper or cloth, replacing sandpaper. Natural garnet is also used for bearings in watches and other delicate instruments because it resists wear.

Of the several kinds of garnet, almandine has the largest industrial use. The only commercially important deposits of this iron garnet occur in the Adirondack Mountains of New York State. There the rock may be as much as 70 percent garnet. The garnet is normally heat-treated to

Minerals have both frivolous and essential uses. FACING: *Color in fireworks comes from minerals, among them antimony and strontium.* TOP: *Fluorite—most of it goes into steel production.* ABOVE: *Stibnite is the chief source of antimony.*

improve its hardness, then crushed, ground, separated by sieves, and graded according to grain size.

FLUORITE: Most highly industrialized countries have adequate supplies of fluorite—known in mining and industry as fluorspar. This is fortunate, since it is now recognized as better than limestone as a flux for making steel. About three-quarters of the world's annual production goes into open-hearth steel furnaces. There it melts easily and combines readily with the impurities in the steel. Once combined, it forms a very liquid and free-flowing slag that can be tapped off. For every ton of steel produced, about six pounds of fluorite is consumed. Fluorite is calcium fluoride (CaF_2); it was named by early metal workers who recognized its ability to flow over impure molten metals and named it for the Latin word "to flow."

Fluorite is used in the ceramics industry to make white enamel coatings for household fixtures and utensils. It is also a starting material for making the refrigerating substance used in automatic refrigerators, an easily liquified gas named sulfur hexafluoride. This gas weighs five times as much as air, is chemically inactive, odorless, colorless, non-poisonous, and will not burn. It is also used as an aerosol gas for spray insecticides,

supplying the pressure to force the contents out of the container as it expands from a liquid to a gaseous state.

Pure, colorless fluorite is only single-refracting, transmits ultraviolet light easily, and has other optical characteristics that are ideal for certain kinds of special lenses. Lead fluoride (PbF_2) has been found to transform electrical energy to light. Fluorite is also the source of fluorine gas, used to prepare many fluorine compounds.

In the United States much fluorite is mined in the rich deposits of southern Illinois and neighboring Kentucky.

ZIRCONIUM: In 1824, Baron Berzelius, a Swedish chemist, prepared the first small, impure sample of this silvery-white metal, which is difficult to extract because it combines easily with oxygen and nitrogen, carbon and silicon, and holds tightly once combined. Through improved purification methods, it has become a valuable industrial and military metal. It makes certain steels shock-and-fatigue-resistant, ideal for machinery that must operate under stress for long periods of time. Because its alloys resist the attack of common acids and chemical solutions it is used, along with alloys of titanium, for bone-repair surgery.

One of the most interesting of industrial uses for zirconium metals is in atomic power installations, where its unique characteristics make it more useful than steel. One of these is thermal stability—ability to withstand the very high temperatures in nuclear reactors without breaking down. Because of zirconium's corrosion resistance, there is no rusting problem. Best of all, zirconium has what is technically called "low neutron capture" characteristics. In order for a nuclear reactor to operate properly, there must be a carefully con-

trolled internal ebb and flow of those fundamental particles called neutrons. Some metals have an unwanted ability to capture some of these neutrons and to interfere with the operation. Zirconium has only one-thirteenth the capturing ability of iron and only one twenty-fifth as much as nickel metal.

The two most important ores of zirconium are the minerals zircon (zirconium silicate) and baddeleyite (zirconium oxide), recovered from beach sands or gravel deposits. The most productive deposits of zircon sand are found at Byron Bay, New South Wales. The best baddeleyite deposits are in the gravels and sands of Minas Gerais,

FACING, TOP: *Vital in other industries, iron—much of it from hematite like this specimen—does not fill new space needs.*
LEFT: *Beryllium is welded to aluminum, magnesium for NASA's Apollo.*
ABOVE: *The satellite Pageos, to orbit 2600 miles above earth.*

They also have a high dielectric strength, meaning that they can act as insulators where very heavy electric charges are involved, without being melted or destroyed, and without leaking off the charge. This accounts for their use in high-quality spark plugs designed to operate at high temperatures. In addition, zirconia does not conduct heat very well, a characteristic that makes it an excellent heat insulator for high-temperature industrial processes. It can also be made into a mineral cloth that will persist indefinitely at a continuous temperature of 3000 degrees Fahrenheit—in fact, that will not melt until it reaches a temperature of 4700 degrees Fahrenheit.

Zirconia has many other uses. Its whiteness and opacity increase the covering power of high-quality enamels. Zirconium carbide (ZrC_2) can be pressed into machine parts that are heat-resistant and more wear-resistant than metal. Zirconium sulfate ($ZrSO_4$) is used for tanning white leather. Sodium zirconium sulfate is used to make good-quality paper very white and very opaque. And finally, the next time you have a bad case of ivy poisoning, it is very likely that you will apply a salve of zirconium carbonate.

STRONTIUM: As with so many metals pressed into modern service, strontium was unknown to the ancients. Not until 1790 was one of its minerals discovered at Strontian, Scotland. It is possible that its two major ores, the minerals celestite, strontium sulfate ($SrSO_4$), and strontianite, strontium carbonate ($SrCO_3$), were used before this date to produce fireworks with bright red colors. This is still one of the chief uses for strontium compounds.

But there are many others. Strontium titanate is made synthetically in clear, colorless crystals that are cut and sold as satisfactory gemstones.

Brazil. Other commercial ore deposits are found in Florida, India, and western Africa.

Most zirconium ore is not used for extracting the metal but is converted to zirconia, which is a pure-white powdered zirconium oxide (ZrO_2). This white substance has a great many uses on its own, and it may also be readily converted to other important zirconium compounds. Ceramic materials made from zirconia can stand temperatures up to 5000 degrees Fahrenheit without melting. They can be made into ceramic parts that will stand much abuse. Zirconia ceramics have a low coefficient of expansion; they can be plunged at white heat into cold water without being damaged.

ABOVE: *Rocket-propellant studies showed these impact patterns made as burning aluminum particles spattered out of the fuel.* FACING, TOP: *Agena target docking vehicle.* RIGHT: *Shock waves during test of beryllium-coated nose cone.*

Another strontium compound is useful in the sugar-beet industry, combining readily with the sugar mixed with sugar-beet molasses to form a solid, strontium saccharate, which is then separated from the liquid molasses. By treating this substance with carbon dioxide gas, the sugar is recovered. The paint industry makes use of powdered celestite which, when added to paint, gives it brightness. There is also a peculiar compound called strontium fluoride (SrF_2) to which is added a small amount of the element samarium as an impurity. This compound is a valuable material for the lasers discussed earlier in this chapter.

SELENIUM: Selenium is a highly poisonous metal.

Plants or foods grown in soils containing sufficient selenium can be toxic. When samples of the selenium-concentrating "loco weed" that grows in some western states have been burned, the selenium recovered has often been found sufficient to poison grazing cattle. Of course, this poisonous characteristic can also be an asset. Selenium is used in insecticides and in special paints for ships' hulls to prevent the growth of algae, barnacles, and other sea life.

The most unusual characteristic of selenium is its electrical behavior. When selenium powder is heated it forms a glassy substance called vitreous selenium. This material is a good conductor of electricity as long as light is shining on it. In darkness, however, it resists the flow of current and is a poor conductor.

Many ingenious applications are made of this characteristic. For example, when the day grows dim a strategically placed selenium cell—or electric eye—develops a resistance to an electric current flowing through it. Eventually as it grows darker the flow of current is reduced enough so that it flips an electric relay switch, and the street lights go on. A similar cell placed at the mouth of a factory smokestack will record the fact that the smoke is too thick and the fires need adjusting.

In another application, a photographer points a selenium-cell meter at his subject. The meter records the changing flow of current from a tiny battery. This tells the photographer how much light there is and what his camera exposure should be. For the long-distance transmission of photographs, a selenium cell is run back and forth over a lighted photograph. It then sends corresponding electrical signals over a wire or by radio broadcast. These signals control a small light source on the other end. This light, traveling over a sensitive photographic plate, will be bright or dark depending on the signal it gets from the selenium cell, and will consequently print an exact long-distance copy of the picture.

Selenium has nonelectrical uses as well. It produces in glass the bright red color needed for danger signals and traffic lights. When added to steels in small amounts it helps improve their machining characteristics for cleaner and easier cutting. Added to lubricating oils, it delays rapid aging and prevents gumminess. Perhaps oddest of all, selenium metal is usually bright and odorless, but when heated and vaporized it becomes putrid. Added to other poisonous gases, like industrial carbon monoxide, it is utilized as a warning of the presence of a poisonous gas leak.

Selenium mineral species are few in number and highly scattered; almost all selenium must be recovered indirectly. Selenium is reclaimed, for example, as a by-product of the copper refineries of the United States and Canada. There are also certain black shales in Idaho that contain as much as one pound per ton of ore.

GERMANIUM AND SILICON: In this electronic age, almost every synthetic and natural material is being investigated to see if it has some kind of electrical property that might be of practical value. Research has opened up a whole new field of practical electronics based on the semiconductors.

Some substances can move their electrons about with great ease—in other words, they conduct electricity very well. Some do not, because their electrons are too rigidly held in place.

Between these conductivity extremes are several elements called semiconductors. Normally they do not conduct an electric current, but with a little help they can be encouraged to perform. This help comes in the form of a small amount of impurity added to certain of these elements as their crystals are being formed. The process is called "doping."

Two of the semiconductors most frequently used are germanium and silicon. These elements look like bright silvery metals, but behave toward most other elements, in their chemical combinations, as if they were not metals. Several elements can be used for doping them. Aluminum, arsenic, and boron are typical and effective. The kind of doping determines what kind of semiconductor will result; there are n-type (negative) and p-type (positive). The major difference between the two types is that they permit what little current flow there is to move in opposite directions.

Space technology has developed new minerals, new uses. FACING, TOP: *Astronaut Edward White's space walk during Gemini 4's 1965 flight.* RIGHT: *Fluorescent dye marks recovery spot as U.S.S. Guam picks up Gemini 11 after its three-day earth orbit in 1966.*

A group of unusually fine specimens of ore minerals.
TOP: *Droplets of native mercury from New Almaden, California.*
ABOVE, LEFT: *Proustite, a ruby silver mineral, from Chile.*
ABOVE, RIGHT: *Dendrites of gold, Grass Valley, California.*
RIGHT: *Chalcotrichite, in whisker crystals from Morenci, Arizona.*

When doped with arsenic, germanium metal is the n-type, and when doped with aluminum it is the p-type. Silicon doped with boron is p-type, with arsenic, n-type.

The most important use for these materials is to replace vacuum tubes in electronic equipment. These semiconductor units consist of doped single crystals. Because of their size and the way they operate, they do not need extravagant amounts of power to heat them up, as vacuum tubes do. They also last much longer and can stand much more stress and punishment than a delicate, assembled vacuum tube, with its many internal parts and glass or metal enclosure.

Best of all, semiconductor units can be very tiny and still very effective. They make possible electronic hearing aids that fit completely inside the ear and pocket radios as small as cigarette packages. Modern electronic computers can contain great numbers of tiny semiconductors, increasing their present use and potential.

The two basic jobs given to semiconductors that replace vacuum tubes are as rectifiers and as amplifiers. Almost all electronic devices use rectifiers, which allow current to flow in one direction only. Arranged in certain combinations, semiconductors perform this function. In other combinations they become the now familiar transistors, which amplify weak current into strong and take the place of the amplifier vacuum tubes formerly essential to most electronic gadgetry.

ANTIMONY: Antimony is one of several elements that sometimes behave as metals and sometimes do not. Arsenic, selenium, tellurium, chromium, tin, manganese, vanadium, tungsten, and molybdenum are in this group. Antimony is used to manufacture "hard lead." Actual lead metal is too soft and bendable for most purposes, so from 4 to 12 percent antimony metal is mixed with it to make it harder. This lead is used to manufacture many items, including storage batteries for automobiles, sheet and pipe for the chemical industry, and protective sheathing for telephone cables. If the percentage of antimony is kept low, thin lead sheet keeps much of its flexibility for such uses as the manufacture of collapsible toothpaste tubes.

Some of the alloys containing antimony are useful because this element leaves them with a smooth surface after casting. Also, these alloys expand slightly on solidifying, so that they can fit tightly to a mold and take on its finest details. Type metal, for linotype and monotype machines, contains 10 to 15 percent antimony. This makes for smooth, well-detailed type and also enables the alloy to melt more easily.

Like most metals, antimony and its compounds have been applied to military uses. Added to lead metal, it hardens shrapnel and bullet cores. The oxide of antimony prevents materials from burning and is used as a fireproofing spray for canvas. As an ingredient in paint mixtures, it makes a nonburning paint for ships. It has also been found that antimony sulfide reflects infrared light just as green tree foliage does. It makes an excellent camouflage paint against spying infrared devices.

Many familiar everyday objects contain antimony. Safety matches have about 3 percent antimony in the match head and 8 percent on the striker. Many new plastic floor tiles contain antimony oxide. Powdered antimony burns with a bluish flame when heated in air—a characteristic that can be seen in every Fourth-of-July fireworks display.

Stibnite (Sb_2S_3) is the most important ore of antimony, although it is also mined as oxides. Bolivia and Mexico are its leading producers.

The Hobby
9

*The amateur mineralogist may,
if he cares to, achieve
near-professional expertise*

By far the greatest number of people involved, in one manner or another, with the mineral kingdom have had no professional training in the subject. More to the point, they have no desire to be professionals. They are interested in the earth sciences as a change of pace from everyday routine, or perhaps as a source of absorbing mental activity. Most people find that mineralogy is a hobby to be taken in doses of any size desired and that its possibilities are inexhaustible.

Recent estimates put the number of organized hobbyists at over seventy-five thousand. The largest of the several earth science hobby magazines, *The Lapidary Journal*, has a monthly circulation of over forty thousand copies. Since most people making collections or working with rocks and minerals are not in organized groups, it is reasonable to assume that they total several times this number.

The volume of sales of supplies, equipment, specimens, and books has reached the status of big business. In contrast with the situation ten or fifteen years ago, it is now possible for a dealer in these materials to make a comfortable living. Hobby dealers catering to the trade find it a full-time commercial activity. There is at least one trade journal, *The Lapidary Reporter*, that keeps the dealers abreast of sources of material, the state of the market, trends in the hobby, and centers of marketing activity. The total num-

ber of known dealers in the United States hovers somewhere around three thousand, but innumerable collectors and part-time dealers are in and out of the market constantly.

A hobbyist may be completely casual—but surprisingly often he slips over the boundary into the status of a scientific professional. Some amateurs develop talents, not common among professionals, for rapid sight recognition of minerals, and can quickly identify several hundred species. The amount of time the hobby absorbs can vary from a little to a lot. There are thousands of rockhounds who spend every weekend and every holiday somewhere in the countryside, chasing after new samples of rocks and minerals. Families often plan their vacation trips around the locations of well-known rock and mineral exposures, and children often develop a rock-collecting hobby of their own through helping to add to the collection of one or both of their parents.

As with any hobby, the amount of money spent is not a direct measure of the enjoyment derived. There are hobbyists who allow themselves several thousand dollars a year for travel and specimen-purchase expenses. There are others who spend practically nothing; they prefer those specimens they can find for themselves and make only a minor investment in equipment. Still others, as a matter of principle, will not purchase any specimen material at all but rely on the shrewd exchanging of self-collected material to build their investment in the hobby.

Since mineralogy deals with objects and their manipulation, participation usually takes the form of making collections. A collection can be very general or very specialized. Some people collect gems, either cutting them in home shops or buying them already cut from dealers. Others

PRECEDING PAGES: *The amateur who starts with an interesting
backyard rock often ends up with the pick, maps, and safety equipment of
the expert field worker—and a growing home laboratory as well.*

collect mineral specimens. Of these, some are "Dana" collectors whose collections include as many as possible of the species that are listed in Dana's *System of Mineralogy*. Collections are also made of minerals from a single mine or quarry. One New Jersey collector has a whole museum of specimens exclusively from the mines at Franklin, New Jersey.

Some collectors prefer single, isolated, well-formed crystals or pseudomorphs or particular chemical groups, such as sulfides or oxides, or even specimens remarkable for their resemblance to sculpture. Back in the 1870s at Lancaster, Pennsylvania, one Reverend Rakestraw became interested in tiny mineral specimens from the iron mines at Cornwall, Pennsylvania. These required magnification to be seen properly, and for their protection he began mounting them in small boxes. He would meet periodically with fellow collectors in Philadelphia, who soon picked up his interest. Unwittingly he triggered a chain of events leading to a cult of several hundred collectors called micromounters, who now hold East and West Coast meetings of their own each year. Aside from the striking beauty of the micromounts, many minerals are simply not available in crystals of larger size and are ideally suited for such collections. Mineral collecting and collections are apparently limited only by the imagination.

Collecting, however, is only one of many areas of activity open to rockhounds. They have found that a number of minerals are suitable for cutting and polishing into gemstones. Most of the easily available material is suitable only for noncommercial objects. However, many kinds of agate and jasper and common rocks found across the country are beautiful when cut and polished. Several of the colors and patterns they display are even

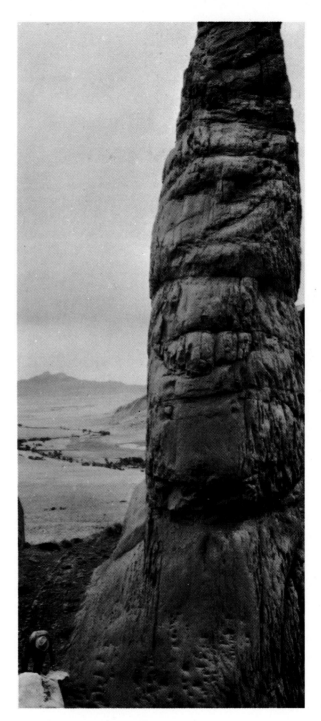

A passing specimen collector pauses in Clarks Fork Canyon, Wyoming, and by contrast points up the size of an eroded pillar of red sedimentary rock.

superior to those of classic decorative minerals that have been cut for centuries and can be creditably exhibited beside such specimens or even in sculpture collections. In an effort to create minor—or even major—treasures, many thousands of amateurs have mastered the lapidary arts. They are turning out exquisite creations, many equal to those produced by European commercial lapidaries during their best years. This craft satisfies the urge for manual work and at the same time provides an outlet for creative, artistic expression.

One of the more recent developments among hobbyists has been the bibliophile group—hobbyists who collect old books and manuscripts concerned with gems and minerals. There are also writers, lecturers, teachers, and a variety of entrepreneurs who have been attracted into the field. Some have no particular mineralogical knowledge, but are interested enough to enjoy mixing socially with those who do and listening to the mineralogical "shop talk."

Amateur mineralogists have a standing not common to amateurs in other fields. They have sometimes led the professional scientists to previously unknown mineral occurrences; they have helped find new species and provide a constant flow of new study material. As an example, many years ago in Colorado Springs a mineral dealer and student of crystallography was intrigued by some crystals he found in material from the mines in Franklin, New Jersey. Familiar though he was with minerals, he could not identify these, and in 1911 brought them to the attention of Dr. Charles Palache at Harvard University. Eventually they were proved to be a newly discovered species. The description was published under the name cahnite after Mr. Lazard Cahn, the discoverer. His achievement was also commemorated on his tombstone, which—by his own direction—was made in the shape of a cahnite crystal.

The hobbyists who become interested in the more technical aspects of mineralogy and geology frequently become amateur scientists, even if not prepared to go the whole way into professionalism. Often they expand into the related fields of chemistry, physics, or mathematics. Even as a diversion, mineralogy offers a purposeful and mentally challenging leisure-time activity—as can be attested to by the professional scientists who began as hobbyists only to find that part-time involvement with this fascinating field was not enough.

The interested amateur soon discovers that he can pursue a variety of activities ranging from entirely physical to entirely mental work. If he

FACING, TOP: *Radioactive torbernite from Aveyron, France—unavailable to collectors.* LEFT: *Crocoite from Tasmania.* ABOVE: *Dolomite from Germany. Pieces similar to these two may still be obtained.*

223

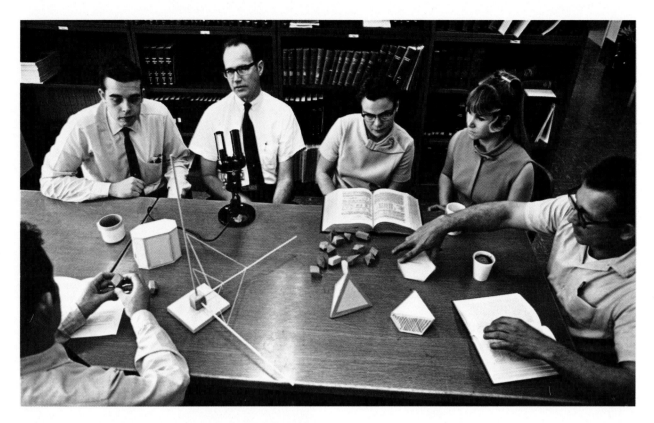

decides to build a mineral collection, he will probably begin a succession of field trips, returning home to find that his work has just begun. Collections build slowly. They consist of the best specimens available at the time from all sources. They must be properly cared for and upgraded when the opportunity arises. This upgrading is a chore in itself; specimens must be cleaned, labeled, catalogued, properly arranged, and stored. Some must be trimmed or repaired; others must be sawed open and polished on exposed surfaces. Specimen preparation has become a fine art and a little appropriate trimming often doubles or triples the quality and the value of the piece.

Aside from these basic curatorial chores, the collector may want to prepare a display cabinet or a fluorescent exhibit or a series of special groupings highlighting perhaps radioactive species or pseudomorphs. He may become excited about

competing in shows; assembling a competitive exhibit is painstaking work. A serious collector, of course, will spend time studying the minerals themselves to enlarge his knowledge.

The collector, in fact, may be much more interested in studying minerals than in collecting them. In this case, he need not enter the mad scramble of competing for high-quality or expensive specimens. He may collect his own, rely on gifts, or purchase less desirable and massive pieces. At home he will have a small laboratory which can become impressive in time. It will probably consist of a mineral table, mineral corner, or mineral alcove, unless he is starting out grandly with a whole mineral room. If properly set up, all his materials, including books, will be handy in one place. There will be a book of mineral tables, a set of hardness-testing minerals or test points, a magnifying glass, a streak plate

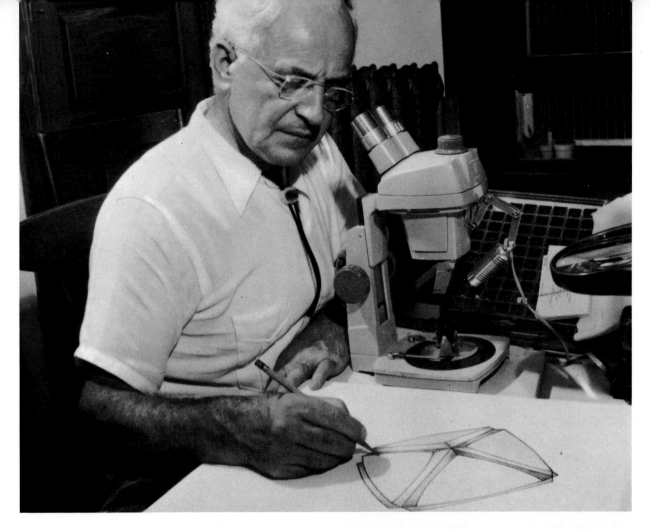

(a rough-surfaced porcelain tile against which the specimen is scratched to reveal the color of the powdered mineral), a magnet, and an ultraviolet light. Later, more expensive equipment will be added—a microscope, a refractometer, and either a manufactured or homemade specific gravity balance. From there on, as he develops competence, other specialized equipment may be added, including a blowpipe and chemical testing equipment and solutions.

When the hobbyist's main interest is in art and craft work, he will find several excellent texts to instruct him. For centuries, professional lapidaries passed the secrets of the trade from generation to generation, keeping tight control over their knowledge of methods. Gradually, however, the secrets were worked out by amateurs and published, and inventive minds turned toward improving and simplifying the old techniques.

FACING: *A Mineral Club study group compares crystals with models.* TOP: *Engineer Paul Seel is an amateur who has become an authority on diamond crystal forms.* ABOVE: *A hobbyist expertly cuts and grinds a cabochon.*

Now the beginner is enriched—or plagued—by a bewildering array of tools, machinery, and advice for all sorts of lapidary endeavors.

It is fascinating for the aficionado to try out new ideas, just as it is for a housewife to try the delicacies in a new cookbook. To start with, he will want a saw for trimming off pieces of rough material to be worked into gems, a grinding wheel for starting cabochons, a sander for fine grinding, and a polishing buff. These may come in combined units with a single motor, or they may be bought separately. Later, faceting equipment may be added. By this time he will be familiar enough with the books and with other lapidaries and dealers to know what further equipment he needs. By this time, also, he will have decided whether his talents lie in making cabochons, faceted stones, carvings, or other lapidary objects. He will know what to look for at sales and what to deal for when trading with other collectors.

Meanwhile he will probably have established contact with other hobbyists who are proficient in precious-metal casting and shaping. A number of amateurs drawn together in this manner have been functioning as new, creative jewelry designers, supplying unique pieces to a growing market. The demand for handcrafted jewelry has enlarged greatly since so many fine materials and new ideas have started to supply it.

Ultimately, all materials used by the hobbyist, except for manufactured equipment and supplies, must come out of the ground. It is surprising how much of it is excavated through amateur activity rather than by professional suppliers for the trade. Every fresh opening in the earth, especially when it cuts through rock, is a potential source. Every mine, mine dump, quarry, stream bed, tunnel, building excavation, or road cut becomes a mecca for collectors. It is almost certain that every new excavation in the last few years has been visited by at least one rummaging hobbyist. Vast tonnages of rock are hauled home to be worked over, reduced in volume and carefully studied; from these treasure troves come many specimens for collections or future lapidary work or even for sale.

The problem of accommodating numbers of visiting rockhounds is often a nuisance to mine and quarry operators. Their response may be unsympathetic—they are likely to declare the properties closed to collectors and to post guards to show they mean it. Nevertheless, there are still ample collecting sites, and new ones are found constantly by questing rockhounds. Planning for these trips often takes on the aspects of a full-scale scientific expedition, involving technical briefings, maps, travel directions, and camping arrangements. On the other hand, the expedition can be as simple as a Sunday afternoon ride in the family car to a rock outcrop in the country. Often the trips are taken in groups sponsored by the local mineral society. There are also highly popular professional tours, led by experienced guides, to exotic collecting grounds in Mexico and Brazil.

The collector's field equipment is usually rather simple. It may consist of a rugged, geologist-type hammer, rock chisels, wrapping paper for specimens, a magnifier for small crystals, a carrying bag, a small notebook, and a first-aid kit. A surprising number of cars traveling on the roads these days keep such simple equipment in the trunk, ready for any opportunity. Of course, there are always some collectors who go equipped for certain special mining chores. It is not unusual, especially in the western states, to come across rockhounds working over an outcropping with dynamite and mining tools, and there are many books to teach them the techniques.

Once the material is out of the ground, the collector saves some of it for immediate or potential use. The rest finds its way into circulation. Depending on the whim of the finder, it is sometimes dispensed as gifts to collectors, schools, or museums, exchanged with other collectors, or even sold to specimen dealers for income or for money to purchase other specimens. Specimen gifts made to friends or children have attracted many new converts to the hobby, and collectors often give away specimens with this object in mind.

TOP: *Pyromorphite from Ems, Germany. Specimens from this old occurrence are still sometimes available.*
ABOVE: *Basic equipment for the amateur laboratory is an inexpensive trim saw, which is fairly easy to master.*

Swapping specimens is as old as commerce itself. A shrewd mineral trader can upgrade his collection substantially if he has the patience and perseverance to carry out the negotiations. A good bit of this exchanging takes place through the mails. All sorts of ingenious packing techniques have been devised by collectors to prevent destruction of specimens in transit. Nesting a tissue-wrapped specimen in a box packed tight with popcorn, or burying the specimen in a box of soap powder, which can be washed off on arrival, are typically ingenious examples.

There are lazier methods of building a collection. The quickest, surest, and easiest way—particularly to acquire special specimens—is to purchase from a dealer. Roadsides, particularly in the West, are peppered with rock shops catering to the transient rockhound trade. Some dealers have set up respectable mail-order business contacts through advertising. Others set up sales booths at rock and mineral shows. Through these, they sell enough to pay expenses, gain a small profit, and at the same time establish new contacts with collectors who become steady customers.

Collectors have long referred to the custom of buying specimens as "silver-picking." High-grading—not in the pejorative sense of the minefields—is another of the terms in the hobby language. It means that the collector has gone over a dealer's stock or a mine dump or a collection being sold and has taken out the best things, leaving the rest for others. Arranging somehow to get at a dealer's new stock and high-grading it before it goes on general sale is a coup every collector dreams about. One dealer, in an attempt to avoid partiality toward any of his customers, used to advertise each year a special sale at a New York hotel. The specimens were laid out on tables, but no one had access to them until the hour of the sale. Several hours in advance, collectors would begin to line up outside. At the given moment the doors were thrown open and the stampede began, with collectors grabbing specimens from the tables and from each other. This kind of special sale was eventually abandoned, with a return to the less hectic, first-come-first-served procedure.

The amount of money being spent on specimens has now reached such proportions that there is tremendous incentive for dealers to obtain more and more material. This in turn has stimulated production on down the line. More specimens are now flowing into the market than at any time before in history. The demand is so great that some mines, not good enough for commercial ore

Amateur field activity can take many productive forms.
ABOVE: *Beachcombing for specimens.* FACING, TOP: *Gold washing in a mountain stream.* RIGHT: *Sieving rubies.*
FAR RIGHT: *Testing for fluorescence in Franklin limestone.*

production, are being operated on a small scale just to produce specimens.

The pressure on the market has also stimulated a creeping inflation of prices. In turn, this has accelerated the rate of supply, because newly mined specimens bring better and better prices. In an effort to eliminate the middleman and his profit, the dealer has tried to get closer to the sources of supply; this has brought higher returns directly to the miners. As an example of the increased activity, years ago only a handful of wholesalers worked regularly through certain active mining areas in Chihuahua, Mexico. These same areas now play host to crowds of buyers each year.

Various sources of information are available to help the collector prepare for field excursions, discover what other collectors are doing, and keep in touch with the dealers. The widely circulated *Lapidary Journal* publishes an extra thick issue every April called the "Rockhound Buyer's Guide." In this hundreds of dealers are listed, cross-indexed to a list of their specialties. This issue also carries pages of advertisements for merchandise of interest to the hobbyist. Everything, from metal jewelry parts or findings to complete camping outfits, is likely to be represented. Reference books are listed, including range guides for particular localities, textbooks, and how-to-do-it books for the lapidary.

Books, of course, are another excellent source of information for the addict. Beyond that, all sorts of usable information can be pried from other collectors, museums, state geological surveys, the United States Geological Survey, state departments of highways, and local chambers of commerce. The avid hobbyist soon becomes expert at quarrying all the information that he needs from every source that is available to him.

The amateur who wishes to join with others who share his dedication has plenty of opportunity. Across the country, there are more than seven hundred amateur societies open to him, varying in size and in specialization but all offering contact with other eager hobbyists. Most of the groups include "Gem and Mineral" in their titles. Some serve a broad range of interests, while others vary from mineral study groups to practical lapidary clubs. In general the western groups, particularly in California, tend to be larger. Some of the societies are sponsored by institutions, some are self-sponsored.

The hobby magazines are the best source for all sorts of club information. They can guide the hobbyist to a club in his area or advise him on how to start one if none exists. Through them, as well as through local newspapers, the hobbyist can keep track of nearby mineral and gem shows, an excellent way of making contact with others interested in the field. For the national picture, the most useful of these magazines are: *The Lapidary Journal*, Box 2369, San Diego, California, 92112; *Rocks and Minerals*, Box 29, Peekskill, New York, 10566; *Earth Science*, Box 550, Downers Grove, Illinois, 60515; *Gems and Minerals*, Gemac Corporation, Box 687, Mentone, California, 92359. Subscribing to one or more of these publications will help to make a seasoned amateur out of the rankest beginner, and put him on the track of further enrichment and pleasure to be obtained from his hobby.

Membership in a well-organized group can greatly enrich the hobbyist's experience. An active club always includes at least a few field trips on its calendar, as well as indoor lectures and demonstrations. Popular and well-informed lec-

Specimens as fine as these can now be found in private high-quality collections. FACING, TOP: *Legrandite from Mapimi, Mexico.* LEFT: *Fluorescing willemite from Franklin.* ABOVE: *Wulfenite from the Glove Mine, Arizona.*

turers move from group to group, heralded by word of mouth and through the magazines. Members are continually improving their information through panel discussions, slide shows, and small serious study groups, and improving their collections through swap sessions and by attending specimen auctions.

Most popular of all amateur activities is the periodic public show. Sometimes the show is held on a local level, but often it is regional or even national.

The numerous earth science and lapidary societies have been organized into six regional federations: the Eastern, Midwestern, Rocky Mountain, Texas, Northwestern, and California federations. Each federation has its own set of officers elected by member clubs. In general, the duties of the regional federation are to help the member societies to thrive. They distribute programming aids and information, conduct scholarship drives, and organize the annual convention and show held in each region. The regional show is usually the

big event of the year. One of the member clubs is always the host, pooling its resources with those of the rest of the federation to provide a memorable event.

A typical regional show will be held in a large convention space. In the center area, many rows of showcases display competitive exhibits entered by individuals and clubs, covering various aspects of the hobby. A set of uniform rules for competition is used throughout the country, setting up nationwide standards for judging. The exhibitor, then, is actually competing with other collectors on a nationwide basis.

The central cases also contain special outstanding exhibitions of various materials that are invited by the show committee for the education and perhaps the envy of conventioneers. These may be a superb suite of large gold goblets, made Cellini-style and studded with precious stones, or a suite of large, polished slabs of perfect specimens of petrified wood. There will always be cases containing previous first-prize exhibits, since an exhibit is permitted to win only once and can be shown again only as a special display.

The dealers' booths—the business part of the show—generally surround the display area. Elbow to elbow, customers and curious onlookers crowd around to look at the latest materials and to window-shop before making final purchases.

By the time the average rockhound leaves the show, he has gorged himself on seeing displays, talking shop, meeting friends, attending nearby field trips, and swapping yarns and specimens. He may also have spent all his money, and been reduced to making mental notes of things he would like to buy next time.

The regional federations themselves are organized into the American Federation of Mineralogical Societies. It assists the regional federations in various ways, maintains the uniform judging rules, and in general oversees the hobby on a national scale. It also sponsors the most important show of the year. Top awards at these shows are considered the pinnacle of success. A

competitor must win a first place in a regional show before he is even allowed to enter into national competition.

Since the show—whether local, regional, or national—is such a vital center of interest, it is not surprising to find a number of enthusiasts traveling from show to show. To accommodate them—and also the various federation officials—all the big shows carefully schedule their dates to avoid overlap.

Considering the great surge in membership and activity among the earth science hobby clubs, the movement appears to have been successfully pursuing its goals. These are very well spelled out in the constitution of the American Federation: "... To promote popular interest and education in the various earth sciences and in particular the subjects of geology, mineralogy, paleontology, lapidary, and other related subjects, and to sponsor and provide means of coordinating the work and efforts of all persons and groups interested therein."

FACING, FAR LEFT: *Copper dendrite from Bolivia.* LEFT: *From a Virginia roadstone quarry, apophyllite on prehnite.* ABOVE: *Diatoms (1000 times enlarged) have plant and animal characteristics, and persistent silica skeletons; they are important rock builders.*

The Connoisseur
10

*Great collections are created
by cultivated taste—assisted by
money to gratify that taste*

According to Webster, an amateur is "one who cultivates a particular pursuit, study, or science, from taste, without pursuing it professionally." A connoisseur is "one esthetically versed in any subject . . . one competent to act as a critical judge of an art, or in a matter of taste."

The amateur, then, can always aspire to connoisseur status—the amateur who can afford the time, who is a true devotee, and who is equipped with or can develop great patience and perseverance. From such collectors come the few who rank as connoisseurs.

The connoisseur's collection eventually abounds in specimens of exceptional quality, beauty, rarity, or scientific importance. He has accomplished this by refining his appreciation of beauty and expanding his knowledge of minerals. He has had to learn about mineral uses, phases, varieties, relationships to rock, relationships to each other, associations, intergrowths, differences of locality habit, and other scientific data.

Few collectors, even among connoisseurs, can afford to be universally well prepared in all these areas. Generally attention must be focused on some special excellence—the physical perfection of the specimens, perhaps, or the completeness of the collection. There are no restrictions, however, and one may specialize or be general as he pleases. Some of the greatest mineral collectors have collected both scientifically and esthetically, with equal success in both of these two areas.

Whenever a great private collection is mentioned, the collector is spoken of as a man of high esthetic sense. Esthetic appreciation is very elusive and difficult to define. Some people just seem to have it and some do not. One certainty is that anyone with this ability is able to compare various objects and to discriminate among them, seeing differences that the less highly trained observer might overlook.

In order to place a value of any kind on any object it is necessary to have something of known value for comparison. Anyone making an evaluation of the beauty of a mineral specimen is in a much better position if he has had broad experience with other mineral specimens. After all, a cat will never win any beauty prizes at a dog show, especially with all the judges knowing only dogs. Every kind of object has its own standards of beauty, which must be thoroughly understood if they are to be applied with any consistency or intelligence.

There is some overlap of esthetic appeal, of course, among various kinds of objects. Among mineral specimens certain forms can be reminiscent of sculpture, and certain color combinations reminiscent of different schools of art. It is possible, then, for collectors with a general appreciation of the arts to assemble collections that are esthetically attractive. Because this kind of esthetic judgment is the easiest and most familiar path toward top-quality specialized collecting, many more collections are founded on esthetically pleasing specimens than are based on scientifically significant ones.

Eventually, the connoisseur faces the critical problem of trying to locate more specimens of the highest beauty. There never have been, and

PRECEDING PAGES: *A collector becomes a connoisseur when he is able to recognize the best of everything that relates to his hobby, for only then can he begin to acquire it.*

are not now, enough of them to satisfy demand. As a result, severe competition for a few specimens continually drives prices higher, making the collector's income the primary instrument of his success in building this connoisseur's kind of collection.

Connoisseurs of mineral specimens can be distinguished from ordinary collectors by the extent of their knowledge of the subject. If there is any common measure for this group it is this combination of knowledge and intelligence. By contact with each other and with the great museums, these mineral collectors have established certain standards for specimen selection: beauty, rarity, perfection of form, scientific importance, and illustration of some natural phenomenon. Specimens

illustrated in this book are entirely within this tradition and have been selected for precisely these reasons. Perhaps the best way to develop a feeling for these criteria is through frequent visits to any of the good museums. Almost all of the important institutional collections of the world are founded on private collections assembled by connoisseurs.

Well-established and securely founded museums are a collector's key to the future. They offer a centrally placed, accessible, properly equipped repository for the preservation of a collection that may have taken a lifetime to build. Such a collection becomes important to posterity. Its dispersion and destruction would be a great waste. The best museums maintain and increase the collections

Many extraordinary amethysts have come from Guerrero, Mexico, an isolated spot from which the finds must be carefully packed out on burro-back. Largest and finest of its kind is the two-foot-high specimen above.

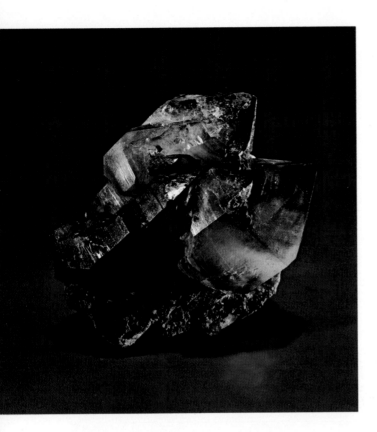

much as the private collector would have done, thus continuing his life's work. They have show collections on public exhibition and study collections in drawers, as most private collectors do. They contact the sources of new specimens and try to acquire them, just as the collector did. By maintaining and improving the collection, they make the original collector's efforts even more worthwhile.

Of American museum collections, three are by far the finest and are among the handful of first-rank collections of the world. They are the collections at the American Museum of Natural History in New York, the Department of Mineralogy of Harvard University in Cambridge, Massachusetts, and the Smithsonian Institution in Washington, D.C. These three have reached their present state of major importance among collections throughout the world because of the prodigious collecting

activities of a comparatively few private collectors.

The tradition of fine private collections of minerals began in the United States about the year 1790 when a botanist, David Hosack, brought a collection to this continent from Europe. Eventually it came into the hands of Princeton University, where it became the first public exhibit of minerals. Later its identity was lost among other collections at Princeton.

The second great American collection is still intact. It was assembled by Adam Seybert (1773-1825), who was the first scientifically trained mineralogist in the country. The Seybert collection is kept in its original cabinet at the Academy of Natural Sciences in Philadelphia. At the same institution is the early collection of Sylvanus Godon, who died in 1812. Another of these early collectors was Gerard Troost (1776-1850), who actually had the honor of studying under Abbé Haüy in Europe. Troost assembled a collection of twenty thousand specimens, which was sold to the Louisville Public Library after his death. Among other early collectors were James Woodhouse (1772-1809), Lardner Vanuxem (1792-1848), Isaac Lea (1792-1880), William Keating (1790-1848), and Thomas Nuttal (1786-1859). The names of these gentlemen appear in the literature of mineralogy, and some have been immortalized by minerals named after them.

All of these collectors were located on the East Coast which, at the time, was the financial, educational, and cultural center of America. Much of the mineral collecting activity centered around Philadelphia. It was not surprising, then, that when the first golden age of American mineral collectors arrived at the end of the century, it centered in the area from Philadelphia northward. Prominent collectors today sometimes speak of mineral

In any field, classics are established by the taste,
experience, and trained eye of the connoisseur. FACING: *Amethyst
from Due West, South Carolina.* ABOVE: *Jan Vermeer's
"Woman Weighing Gold." Both classics are in national museums.*

collecting "in the old Philadelphia tradition."

The group of collecting titans of this period included Washington A. Roebling, Frederick A. Canfield, Clarence S. Bement, George Vaux, Magnus Vonsen, and A. F. Holden. Each of these men assembled a collection sufficient in itself for an entire museum. Perhaps the most important private collection that was ever assembled in the United States belonged to Washington A. Roebling (1837-1926).

Colonel Roebling was an engineer who is remembered for building the Brooklyn Bridge and for his mineral collection. He was made an invalid by an attack of the bends, which occurred while he was working in the caissons under the East River during construction of the Brooklyn Bridge. Because of this, he did much of his col-

lecting by correspondence from his home in New Jersey. With sufficient wealth and ample time to work at it, he set very elaborate and worthwhile goals for his collecting activities. It was his intention to collect a sample of every well-described mineral species then known to man. By the time of his death he had come within a dozen specimens of his goal. In addition, he had gathered together hundreds of examples of varieties of these species from thousands of different occurrences around the world. Many of these specimens were of extraordinary beauty, unique in size or form or some other characteristic.

In the process of collecting, the Colonel became extremely knowledgeable about minerals and skilled at mineral identification. He made a point of offering his specimens for the use of mineral scientists of the day and knew most of these men personally. When he died in 1926 his son, John Roebling, gave the collection of sixteen thousand specimens to the Smithsonian, which already had a good, but not superior, collection. Overnight, with this gift, the Institution's collection gained rank with the leaders of the world.

That same year the Smithsonian received the Canfield collection. This collection's history began in the early 1800s, when Mahlon D. Dickerson began to assemble a fine collection of minerals at his home in Dover, New Jersey. These were from various world occurrences, but luckily included some of the better and highly interesting mineral specimens that were being found at the time in New Jersey.

On Mr. Dickerson's death the collection went to his nephew, Frederick Canfield, Sr., who built it into a fine collection of sixteen hundred pieces. Many of these again were from the famous zinc mines at Franklin, New Jersey. Mr. Canfield's professional connection with the mines gave him access to this material and he assembled what remains the finest collection made from these mines. On his death, the collection passed to his son, Frederick A. Canfield, Jr., also a mineral collector. Keeping the original collection intact, the new owner began to assemble one of his own, which he built to a total of nine thousand specimens. This was also a worldwide collection, but was very rich in newly recovered, fine specimens from New Jersey.

Canfield subsidized workmen in railway tunnels, stone quarries, and road construction to collect specimens for him. Like Roebling, he became very knowledgeable about specimens in the process of collecting them. At his death, having no heirs, he willed the entire collection to the Smithsonian,

along with an endowment for its increase and improvement.

With the Roebling and Canfield collections arriving in the same year, the Smithsonian was barely able to cope. But by the time the collections were absorbed a magnificent nucleus had been established to which, as time went on, other private collections have been added. Without question, the Smithsonian's National Collection of Minerals has been the result of the initial work of amateurs and connoisseurs.

When A. F. Holden graduated from Harvard University in 1888, he was best known as a famous football player. But he had been trained as a mining engineer, and soon became wealthy at his profession. Meanwhile he had developed a love for minerals, which he started to collect

FACING: *In 1799, Philadelphia was already becoming a mineral-collecting center. Connoisseurs from the area who later founded museum collections were,* TOP: *W. A. Roebling;* ABOVE, LEFT: *C. S. Bement;* ABOVE, RIGHT: *F. A. Canfield, Jr.*

seriously in 1895. In a short time his collection was one of the best in the country. Like Roebling, Holden was not interested in mineral species only as showy specimens. Nevertheless his collection does contain hundreds of small but beautiful specimens as well as great numbers of species samples. In 1913 he willed the collection, with an endowment, to Harvard University. This gave Harvard's collection the leading position it now holds among collections of mineral specimens to be found in American universities.

The other of the three major institutional collections, at the American Museum of Natural History in New York, achieved its status by the same means. Most important among its collections is one assembled by Clarence S. Bement, a wealthy Philadelphia manufacturer who searched out beautiful and exceptional specimens of their kind. His collection did not contain the broad sweep of species that distinguished the Roebling and Holden collections. However, by the end of the 1800s it was rated the highest-quality collection in the United States and among the finest anywhere in the world. Losing interest about 1900, Bement sold his collection to J. Pierpont Morgan of New York, who presented it to the American Museum. Many of its fine old specimens are still the best of their kind in existence.

No listing of great private collectors would be complete without reference to the Vaux family of the Philadelphia area. William Vaux (1811-1882) was one of the earliest of this rising group of wealthy connoisseurs. In his time, his collection was considered the finest in America. It was not surpassed until the time of Bement. Upon his death, the William Vaux collection was willed to the Academy of Natural Sciences in Philadelphia, where it is now the backbone of the Academy's excellent collection.

Before the collection went to the Academy, Vaux's son, George Vaux, selected from it certain specimens for himself, as he had been instructed to do. This nucleus stimulated the heir into building a collection of his own, which soon became a major one. George Vaux Jr. continued the effort until the final collection surpassed that of his grandfather. It was given to Bryn Mawr College, automatically placing this college collection among the more important ones.

During this age of great collectors almost all the collections were being established in the eastern part of the country. However, in Petaluma, California, Magnus Vonsen (1879-1954) began assembling a major collection about the time of World War I. Like all the other collectors he had the means, the time, and the interest necessary. Also, like the others, he became very knowledgeable in the process. It was his dream that eventually a great public collection would be established on the West Coast, and to further the idea he willed his collection to the California Academy of Sciences, which displays it in a museum in Golden Gate Park in San Francisco.

The pattern holds true in museums around the world. The famed British Museum, repository for many private collections, recently received the Sir Arthur Russell collection, which contains unsurpassed specimens of minerals from British mines. The Natural History Museum of Stockholm has the beautiful Sjogren collection in its handsome inlaid wood cases. Excellent private collections are being made right now in various parts of the

world. Some will eventually go to museums as they have in the past.

The Natural History Museum in Paris has the magnificent collection of Colonel Louis Vesignié, who died in 1954. It is worth stopping to consider Colonel Vesignié as the prototype of the true connoisseur—a collector whose energy, taste, and discrimination made him a spiritual descendant of those enlightened amateurs of the eighteenth and nineteenth centuries.

In 1956, the "Bulletin de la Société Française de Minéralogie et de Cristallographie" printed a memorial article on Colonel Vesignié, describing him as "a passionate mineralogist." It is translated here, in part, because it offers almost a blueprint for the attitudes and equipment of the top-rank connoisseur.

"[Colonel Vesignié's] collection of crystallized minerals is among the most beautiful amateur collections in the world. At an estimate, it contains about 40,000 specimens. . . . His collection of precious stones is equally remarkable. It includes a series of pegmatite gems of which certain specimens are exceptional for their size and clarity; they are now displayed in the mineralogy gallery of the [Paris Natural History] Museum, where one can see along with other cut stones a 377-carat blue topaz from Siberia, a 250-carat rose beryl from Madagascar, and a superb alexandrite of about 100 carats. . . . He had brought together also a fine collection of meteorites, and he watched for the announcement of new falls to acquire good samples of them. . . . Colonel Vesignié sought after rare specimens, not only to please his eyes and for the satisfaction of being the sole owner of a unique specimen, but also for truly scientific reasons. In fact, from his conversation, it was easy to detect his perfect knowledge of mineral species, their

FACING: *This seven-inch azurite crystal is one of the finest of many superb specimens from the copper mines at Tsumeb, South Africa. Mining here has passed the oxidized zone that produced such crystals; no more are likely to emerge.*

modes of occurrence and association. This knowledge and these aptitudes are reflected in the composition of his collection, where natural series and paragenetic minerals are perfectly represented from the basic species to the rare ones."

It is not only the wealthy who are able to participate in such endeavors. The fact that so many people of modest means are making fine collections is good evidence that wealth is not necessary. True, such collections do not become as large as those of affluent collectors, nor do they grow as quickly, but they can be every bit as good. Sometimes they command notice in their own right. Often, they are absorbed into other collections until, in aggregate, they form a single major collection. Such collecting can readily be done today and the specimens to make up such a collection are constantly available.

Collectors have no difficulty in finding good representative specimen material. It is the connoisseur who has the problem, because he must restrict himself to the rare and beautiful specimens that are so hard to get.

Several attempts have been made to develop a scientific method of appraisal as an aid in evaluating the desirability of a mineral specimen. This has been done in the belief that value and desirability are closely related in our economic system. No attempt has been too serious and none completely successful. Judgment of fine specimens is still a cultivated art—one that takes considerable time and effort to develop.

George L. English, a noted mineral dealer, relates the story of the purchase by Clarence S. Bement of an excellent collection owned by Norman Spang of Etna, Pennsylvania, sometime around 1880. Each man made a personal appraisal of the collection in an attempt to arrive at a satisfactory agreement. Although the total was nearly $22,000, the two men were only a hundred dollars apart in their estimates. This indicates that there was a common set of values subtly accepted by both collectors. Other incidents of this kind occur frequently throughout the years, affirming that there are some unconsciously recognized factors controlling the desirability and therefore the value of specimens. George English suggests that these are commercial value, chemical composition, form, rarity, and a few other miscellaneous characteristics —beauty, size, hardness, uniqueness, and associated minerals. At first glance these seem reasonable factors for judging, but in every case the effect on specimen value is arguable.

For example, a thousand-pound crystal of beryl has considerable value if sold as an ore of beryllium. However, aside from its possible desirability to a museum or two, there is hardly anything less salable as a specimen for a collection than a crude thousand-pound crystal of any species. Its value, therefore, is only as much as the ore is worth. No collector would pay a premium price for it as a desirable specimen because its bulk, weight and roughness make it undesirable for a private collection. On the other hand, a one-ounce well-formed crystal of gold has a commercial value of only thirty-five dollars as gold bullion, but carries a large premium value for collectors. Large gold crystals are rare and attractive. A one-inch, lustrous, twinned crystal of cumengite has no commercial value whatsoever and yet among connoisseurs it is infinitely more desirable than gold and diamonds and brings equivalent prices. Commercial ore value, then, has little if any effect on the degree of desirability of a specimen.

George English also tried to make a case for the effect of chemical composition on specimen

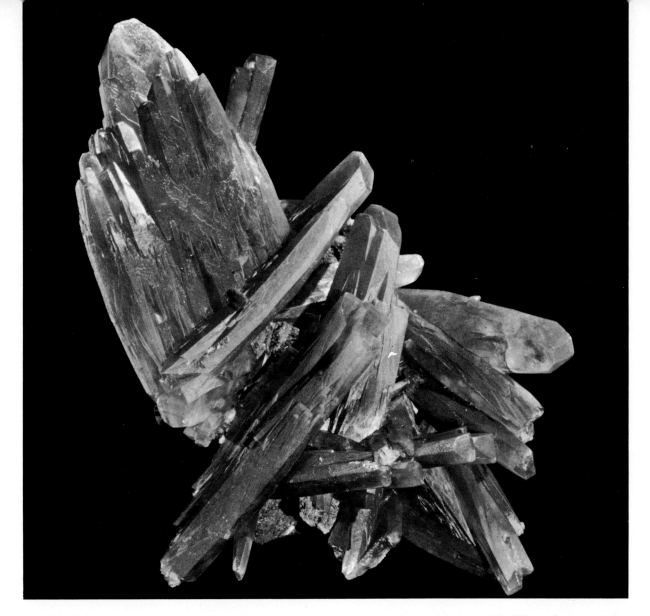

value. Here he increases the confusion by considering the premium value of rare chemical substances while also making allowances for commercial ore value. There is a good reason, however, for considering chemical composition as a determiner of value. Some substances are very rare. Newly described species particularly are in short supply. Collectors have difficulty getting them. This tends to heighten their desirability, even when they have little else to recommend them. The chemical composition in this case is only indirectly the cause; it is rarity that is the immediate consideration.

Specimen form certainly influences value. Every educated collector knows that specimens with large, perfect crystals and brilliant faces are the most valuable. This seems to apply regardless of the species. Species like quartz and calcite, even though very common, are generally much preferred to rarer or more unusual species that just do not occur in good crystals. The perfection and size of the crystals, and freedom from damage, distortion, coatings, and inclusions, all have direct and strong bearing on value.

There are all sorts of variations on this theme. Specimens with crystals attractively scattered on rock are usually better than those with crystals closely bunched. Specimens with a few large crystals are better than those with a druse of many small ones. When a species does not occur

Mines at Alston Moor, Frizington, and elsewhere in Cumberland, England, once produced many exceptional barite specimens like the one above. An occasional piece may still be obtainable from a dealer or an old collection.

with crystals, any attractive form it may exhibit increases its value. Botryoidal hematite, stalactitic limonite, reticulated cerussite, coralloidal aragonite, and globular pectolite are all more desirable than formless masses of the same minerals.

Rarity, like form, also seems to have a direct effect on the value of a specimen. Two kinds of rarity are generally recognized. One is the rarity of a specimen's high superiority. Very fine specimens, with all the requirements of crystal perfection, crystal arrangement, freedom from damage, and size of crystals, are exceedingly rare. The other kind of rarity is due to scarcity of the species or of a particular variety having unusual color or form. Good crystals of garnets in dodecahedron form are common, but a well-formed cube of garnet—a legitimate crystallographic possibility—is rare indeed. George English, in his treatment of rarity, admits that when "superlatively fine crystals of a mineral occur in great abundance" their value, based on the rarity of high quality, collapses.

All other miscellaneous factors determining price boil down to qualities contributing to the durability and beauty of the specimen. Beauty, in particular, seems to have a strong effect on specimen value, perhaps more than anything else. Admittedly, beauty is indefinable. Two specimens of the same mineral, almost identical in size, number of crystals, luster, and perfection of condition, may be wide apart in beauty. One may have transparent crystals of soft pink color and the other may be opaque and dull gray-green. Color, shape, arrangement, transparency, neatness, and other subtle and related factors contribute to estimates of beauty. The collector with a cultured esthetic taste will recognize the necessary combinations of these attributes at a glance.

By far the most overwhelming effect on specimen value is created by the operation of the laws of supply and demand. The mineral specimen market is now large enough so that prices for desirable specimens are controlled by market conditions. Successful mineral dealers know their customers and their customers know each other. A balance is struck. The dealer will recover for his specimens what he knows the collectors will pay. Collectors on the other hand will pay what is necessary to keep all fine specimens from going into the hands of their competitors. The limit seems to be how badly the collector wants the specimen, based on his judgment of how rare or beautiful it is. This aspect of collecting does not lend itself to analysis; it remains an art. The most successful artists build the finest collections.

The true connoisseur, then, is not satisfied with simply accumulating specimens of great beauty, rarity, or perfection of crystal form. He also wants to know the life history of his specimens, the conditions under which they formed, and the natural transformations and processes they have been through. In his collecting activity he finds great peace and relief from the monotony and pressures of his business or profession, as well as an exciting mental tonic. He browses around mineral dealer displays, wanders in and out of their shops, visits auction houses, antique and used furniture shops, other collections, museums, mines, quarries, road cuts—any place that hints of a source of specimens. Through his hobby he is enjoying a fascinating cultural activity and at the same time he is increasing his knowledge of the mineral kingdom. And very likely—because of his deep acquaintance with the earth and its products—he understands the mineral foundation that is the basis of our industrial civilization.

Even museums must now compete for specimens of this quality. (a) Stibiconite replacing stibnite, from San Luis Potosí, Mexico. (b) Pyromorphite from the Merkur Mine, Ems, Germany. (c) Mimetite from Cumberland, England. (d) Proustite from Chanarcillo, Chile.

a

b

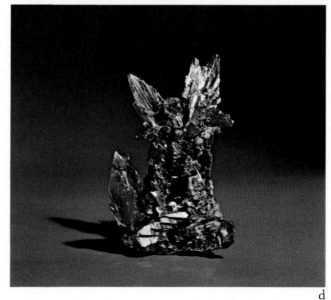

c

d

247

Index

Credits

The publisher wishes to thank the Smithsonian Institution and its staff for assistance in providing many of the subjects for photographs in this book; thanks are due to Mrs. Robert Dunning for her photo research, and to Dr. Peter Leavens for his expert reading of the manuscript. All photographs by Lee Boltin, other than:

Pages 2-3—Jack Kath, Smithsonian Institution; Pages 6-7—L. Perloff, Smithsonian Institution.

CHAPTER ONE: 13—*De Re Metallica*, Basel, 1556; 16—*Hortus Sanitatis*, 1491; 17—*Through Alchemy to Chemistry* by John Read, published by G. Bell & Sons, Ltd.; 18—Horse-Collar from Mammen, The National Museum of Denmark; 20, left—Metropolitan Museum of Art, Rogers Fund, 1916, and contribution of Henry Walters; 20, right—Metropolitan Museum of Art, the Cesnola Collection, purchased by subscription, 1874-76; 20, bottom—The American Numismatic Society, New York; 21, left—in the Brooklyn Museum Collection; 25—Culver Pictures, Inc.; 26—Tom Hollyman, Photo Researchers, Inc.; 27, top—L. Perloff, Smithsonian Institution; 29—Smithsonian Institution; 32-33, top—U.S. Department of the Interior, National Park Service.

CHAPTER TWO: 38—Culver Pictures, Inc.; 39—Smithsonian Institution; 40—Jack Kath, Smithsonian Institution; 42—*Les Pierres Précieuses* by J. P. Rambosson, 1870; 50, left and 51—Smithsonian Institution; 52 and 53—L. Perloff, Smithsonian Institution; 55, bottom—*Corso di Mineralogia* by Luigi Bombicci, 1862; 59—Charles Gardner; 62-63—Jack Kath, Smithsonian Institution; 65—Charles Gardner; 66—L. Perloff, Smithsonian Institution.

CHAPTER THREE: 70-71—Boltin, courtesy of Harry Winston; 73, top—*An Introduction to a History of Woodcut* by Arthur M. Hind, Dover Publications, Inc., New York, 1963. Reprinted through permission of the publisher; 73, bottom—*The Mirror of Stones* by Camillus Leonardus, 1520; 74—the Pierpont Morgan Library; 75—J. Scott, Smithsonian Institution; 76—Metropolitan Museum of Art, purchased by subscription, 1895; 77—*Grundriss der Edelsteinkunde* by P. H. Groth, 1887; 79—J. Scott, Smithsonian Institution; 80-81—*Les Pierres Précieuses* by J. P. Rambosson, 1870; 81, right—Smithsonian Institution; 83, top—the University Museum of the University of Pennsylvania; 84—N. W. Ayer & Son, Inc.; 85—Boltin, courtesy of Harry Winston; 86—*Les Pierres Précieuses* by J. P. Rambosson, 1870; 87—South African Information Service; 88—Smithsonian Institution; 89—*Precious Stones and Gems* by E. W. Streeter, 1877; 90—*Les Pierres Précieuses* by J. P. Rambosson, 1870; 91—Smithsonian Institution; 93—J. Scott, Smithsonian Institution; 94 and 95—the American Museum of Natural History; 96, bottom—J. Scott, Smithsonian Institution; 98—The Louvre, Paris; 99—J. Scott, Smithsonian Institution; 100—*Minéralogie Appliquée Aux Arts* by C. P. Brard, 1821; 101—*Les Pierres Précieuses* by J. P. Rambosson, 1870; 102—J. Scott, Smithsonian Institution; 103—K. Jensen, Smithsonian Institution; 105—Gemological Institute of America.

CHAPTER FOUR: 109—Culver Pictures, Inc.; 110 and 111—Smithsonian Institution; 113—*Introductory Course of Natural Philosophy* by W. G. Peck, 1873; 116, top—Culver Pictures, Inc.; 116, bottom—*Minerals from Earth and Sky* by G. P. Merrill & W. F. Fosbag, 1929; 117, left—Culver Pictures, Inc.; 117, right—*The New Knowledge* by R. K. Duncan, 1905; 118—*Les Pierres* by L. Simonin, 1869; 119, top—Paul Seel; 119, bottom—Smithsonian Institution; 120-121—Smithsonian Institution; 124, top—John Farrell, Smithsonian Institution; 124, bottom, and 125—Smithsonian Institution; 127, right, top and bottom—L. Perloff, Smithsonian Institution; 128—Smithsonian Institution.

CHAPTER FIVE: 130-131—William A. Garnett; 133—*Bilderbuch für Kinder* by Bertuch; 135—published by permission of the Trustees of the British Museum; 137, top—Van Bucher, Photo Researchers, Inc.; 138-139—"Harper's" magazine, 1873; 142, left—*Cyclopedia of Universal History* by Ridpath, 1887; 142, right—Australian News & Information Bureau; 143—Culver Pictures, Inc.; 146, top—Culver Pictures, Inc.; 146, bottom—Smithsonian Institution; 147—Joseph Munroe, Photo Researchers, Inc.; 148, bottom—The Freeport Sulphur Co.; 150-151—Chile Exploration Company.

CHAPTER SIX: 155—the Pierpont Morgan Library; 160, top—"Mandolin and Guitar," the Solomon R. Guggenheim Museum, New York City.

CHAPTER SEVEN: 166-167—Jack Kath, Smithsonian Institution; 169—*Meyer's Grosses Konversations Lexikon*, Leipzig, 1897; 170, top—Smithsonian Institution; 170, bottom—*Les Pierres* by L. Simonin, 1869; 171—"Penny," 1833; 172—Culver Pictures, Inc.; 173—*History of Science and Technology and Philosophy in the 16th & 17th Century* by A. Wolfe, published by George Allen & Unwin Ltd.; 174—Bibliothèque Nationale, Paris: courtesy of American Heritage Publishing Co.; 175—U.S. Navy; 176—*Les Pierres* by L. Simonin, 1869; 177—National Park Service; 178-179—Fritz Henle, Photo Researchers, Inc.; 185, bottom—Smithsonian Institution.

CHAPTER EIGHT: 193—The Bettmann Archive, Inc.; 194—"Journal of Chemical Education"; 195—Swedish Information Service; 196—*London* edited by Charles Knight, 1842; 197—New York Public Library; 198, left—Glass Container Manufacturing Institute; 198, right—Culver Pictures, Inc.; 199—The Anaconda Company; 201—Tom Hollyman, Photo Researchers, Inc.; 202—Frederick Ayer, Photo Researchers, Inc.; 203—UPI; 206, top—Van Bucher, Photo Researchers, Inc.; 207—Bell Telephone Labs, Inc.; 208—F. Grunzweig, Photo Researchers, Inc.; 210, bottom—NASA; 211 through 215—NASA.

CHAPTER NINE: 221—Marvin Winter, Photo Researchers, Inc.; 224—A. Edge Goldstein; 225, top—Paul Seel; 225, center, bottom—A. Edge Goldstein; 228—A. Edge Goldstein; 229, top—Carl Fisher, Photo Reasearchers, Inc.; 229, bottom left and right—A. Edge Goldstein; 232 and 233—Smithsonian Institution.

CHAPTER TEN: 239—"A Woman Weighing Gold," Jan Vermeer: the National Gallery of Art; 240—New York Public Library; 241—Smithsonian Institution.